2000	1999	1998	1997								
4	3	4	5	4	3	3	3	3	2	5	'89, '88, '83, '76, '71, '61, '59
4	4	3	4	3	4	4	3	2	3	3	'82, '75, '61
5	4	3	4	4	4	3	1	1		5	'89, '85, '82, '75, '61, '59, '53
4	4	4	4	4	4	2	1	1	1	5	'89, '83, '75, '67, '59, '55, '49
3	5	3	3	4	4	2	4	2	3	5	'78, '69, '59, '49, '45
4	4	3	4	5	5	3	3	4	2	4	'86, '66, '62, '47
3	3	4	3	4	5	2	3	3	2	5	'88, '85, '82, '71, '64, 59, '52
3	3	3	4	4	3	3	3	2	2	5	'89, '76, '71, '64, '59, '49
4	5	4	4	4	3	1	2	4		5	'89, '85, '83, '78, '71, '69, '61
5	4	5	3	3	4	3	3	2	2	5	'89, '85, '83, '78, '70, '61
5	4	5	3	5	5	4	5	4	3	3	'80, '82, '85
3	3	3	3	4	5	5	3	3	4	3	'87, '85, '82, '78, '75, 70, '68
4	5	4	3	5	5	4	2	3	4	3	'86, '81
5	5	4	5	5	4	2	3	1	2	5	'89, '85, '82, '78, '75, '68, '62
4	5	4	5	2	4	3	4	1	3	5	'88, '85, '82, '75, '71, 70, '63
5		3	4	2	2	5		4	4		'76, '70, '66, '63, '55, '45
3	4	4	4	3	4	4	4	4	3	5	'76, '75, '71, '64, '59, '53
4	5	3	5	2	4	4	3	3	1	5	'86, '85, '69, '47
3	3	5	3	5	4	4	2	3	4	4	'86, '82, '76, '71, '63, '59
4	4	5	4	4	3	4	2	3	4	3	
4	4	2	4	4	5	3	4	3	3	4	
4	2	4	5	4	4	2	3	3	3	4	
3	3	4	3	2	4	3	3	4	3	2	'87
3	4	3	5	4	4	5	4	4	4	4	'85, '74, '69, '68, '65, 58, '51
4	4	4	4	4	4	4	3	4	4	4	
4	5	4	3	3	2	5	4	4	4	4	'83, '75
4	4	4	3	3	3	4	4	4	3	4	'83

Vintage charts are helpful to jog your memory or satisfy your curiosity about what years were *generally* best in a particular region. They're less useful in helping select a specific wine as good producers can make decent wines even in in poor years.

WINE NOTES

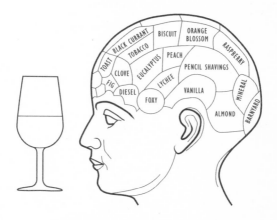

Wine is like music – it's nice in the background, but if you want to learn about it, a little focus is necessary.

WINE TASTING NOTEBOOK

By Steve De Long

with special thanks to: Tyler Colman, Deborah De Long, Michael Gitter, Richard Leahy, Eric Lecours, Toby Riddel, Arthur Stein, Ben Schmerler and JC Viens for their invaluable input

SECOND EDITION

ISBN 978-1-936880-00-3
Printed in China
© 2007, 2011 De Long Company

For more high quality winemaps, charts and books, visit
www.delongwine.com

DE LONG

tasting date: location:

tasting partner(s):

wine name:

producer:

region/appellation:

grape varieties:

vintage: alcohol: price:

COLOR DEPTH:
watery | pale | medium | deep | dark

COLOR HUE:
WHITE: greenish | yellow | straw yellow | gold | amber
RED: purplish | ruby | red | garnet | brick | brown
ROSÉ: pink | salmon | orange | copper

CLARITY:
clear | slight haze | cloudy

AROMA INTENSITY:
low | moderate | aromatic | powerful

DEVELOPMENT:
youthful | some age | aged

AROMAS:

DRY/SWEET:
bone dry | dry | off dry | medium sweet | sweet | very sweet

BODY:
very light | light | medium | medium-full | full-bodied | heavy

ACIDITY:
tart | crisp | fresh | smooth | flabby

TANNINS (IF PRESENT):
LEVEL: low | medium | high   TYPE: soft | round | dry | hard

BALANCE:
good | fair | unbalanced (excess: alcohol - acid - tannin - sugar)

FLAVOR INTENSITY:
low | moderate | flavorful | powerful

FLAVORS:

FINISH:
short (< 3 sec) | medium (4-5) | long (5-7) | v. long (>8 sec)

CONCLUSION:

STYLE:
traditional | in-between | modern

rating: ☆ ☆ ☆ ☆ ☆

FOOD: **FOOD PAIRING:**
                    MATCH: perfect | good | neutral | bad

tasting date: location:

tasting partner(s):

wine name:

producer:

region/appellation:

grape varieties:

vintage: alcohol: price:

COLOR DEPTH:
watery | pale | medium | deep | dark

COLOR HUE:
WHITE: greenish | yellow | straw yellow | gold | amber
RED: purplish | ruby | red | garnet | brick | brown
ROSÉ: pink | salmon | orange | copper

CLARITY:
clear | slight haze | cloudy

AROMA INTENSITY:
low | moderate | aromatic | powerful

DEVELOPMENT:
youthful | some age | aged

AROMAS:

DRY/SWEET:
bone dry | dry | off dry | medium sweet | sweet | very sweet

BODY:
very light | light | medium | medium-full | full-bodied | heavy

ACIDITY:
tart | crisp | fresh | smooth | flabby

TANNINS (IF PRESENT):
LEVEL: low | medium | high   TYPE: soft | round | dry | hard

BALANCE:
good | fair | unbalanced (excess: alcohol - acid - tannin - sugar)

FLAVOR INTENSITY:
low | moderate | flavorful | powerful

FLAVORS:

FINISH:
short (< 3 sec) | medium (4-5) | long (5-7) | v. long (>8 sec)

CONCLUSION:

STYLE:
traditional | in-between | modern

rating: ☆ ☆ ☆ ☆ ☆

FOOD: **FOOD PAIRING:**
                    MATCH: perfect | good | neutral | bad

tasting date: location:

tasting partner(s):

wine name:

producer:

region/appellation:

grape varieties:

vintage: alcohol: price:

COLOR DEPTH:
watery | pale | medium | deep | dark

COLOR HUE:
WHITE: greenish | yellow | straw yellow | gold | amber
RED: purplish | ruby | red | garnet | brick | brown
ROSÉ: pink | salmon | orange | copper

CLARITY:
clear | slight haze | cloudy

AROMA INTENSITY:
low | moderate | aromatic | powerful

DEVELOPMENT:
youthful | some age | aged

AROMAS:

DRY/SWEET:
bone dry | dry | off dry | medium sweet | sweet | very sweet

BODY:
very light | light | medium | medium-full | full-bodied | heavy

ACIDITY:
tart | crisp | fresh | smooth | flabby

TANNINS (IF PRESENT):
LEVEL: low | medium | high   TYPE: soft | round | dry | hard

BALANCE:
good | fair | unbalanced (excess: alcohol - acid - tannin - sugar)

FLAVOR INTENSITY:
low | moderate | flavorful | powerful

FLAVORS:

FINISH:
short (< 3 sec) | medium (4-5) | long (5-7) | v. long (>8 sec)

CONCLUSION:

STYLE:
traditional | in-between | modern

rating: ☆ ☆ ☆ ☆ ☆

FOOD: **FOOD PAIRING:**
                         MATCH: perfect | good | neutral | bad

tasting date: location:

tasting partner(s):

wine name:

producer:

region/appellation:

grape varieties:

vintage: alcohol: price:

COLOR DEPTH:
watery | pale | medium | deep | dark

COLOR HUE:
WHITE: greenish | yellow | straw yellow | gold | amber
RED: purplish | ruby | red | garnet | brick | brown
ROSÉ: pink | salmon | orange | copper

CLARITY:
clear | slight haze | cloudy

AROMA INTENSITY:
low | moderate | aromatic | powerful

DEVELOPMENT:
youthful | some age | aged

AROMAS:

DRY/SWEET:
bone dry | dry | off dry | medium sweet | sweet | very sweet

BODY:
very light | light | medium | medium-full | full-bodied | heavy

ACIDITY:
tart | crisp | fresh | smooth | flabby

TANNINS (IF PRESENT):
LEVEL: low | medium | high   TYPE: soft | round | dry | hard

BALANCE:
good | fair | unbalanced (excess: alcohol - acid - tannin - sugar)

FLAVOR INTENSITY:
low | moderate | flavorful | powerful

FLAVORS:

FINISH:
short (< 3 sec) | medium (4-5) | long (5-7) | v. long (>8 sec)

CONCLUSION:

STYLE:
traditional | in-between | modern

rating: ☆ ☆ ☆ ☆ ☆

FOOD: **FOOD PAIRING:**

MATCH: perfect | good | neutral | bad

tasting date: location:

tasting partner(s):

wine name:

producer:

region/appellation:

grape varieties:

vintage: alcohol: price:

COLOR DEPTH:
watery | pale | medium | deep | dark
COLOR HUE:
WHITE: greenish | yellow | straw yellow | gold | amber
RED: purplish | ruby | red | garnet | brick | brown
ROSÉ: pink | salmon | orange | copper
CLARITY:
clear | slight haze | cloudy

AROMA INTENSITY:
low | moderate | aromatic | powerful
DEVELOPMENT:
youthful | some age | aged
AROMAS:

DRY/SWEET:
bone dry | dry | off dry | medium sweet | sweet | very sweet
BODY:
very light | light | medium | medium-full | full-bodied | heavy
ACIDITY:
tart | crisp | fresh | smooth | flabby
TANNINS (IF PRESENT):
LEVEL: low | medium | high   TYPE: soft | round | dry | hard
BALANCE:
good | fair | unbalanced (excess: alcohol - acid - tannin - sugar)
FLAVOR INTENSITY:
low | moderate | flavorful | powerful
FLAVORS:

FINISH:
short (< 3 sec) | medium (4-5) | long (5-7) | v. long (>8 sec)
CONCLUSION:

STYLE:
traditional | in-between | modern

rating: ☆ ☆ ☆ ☆ ☆

FOOD: **FOOD PAIRING:**
MATCH: perfect | good | neutral | bad

tasting date: location:

tasting partner(s):

wine name:

producer:

region/appellation:

grape varieties:

vintage: alcohol: price:

COLOR DEPTH:
watery | pale | medium | deep | dark

COLOR HUE:
WHITE: greenish | yellow | straw yellow | gold | amber
RED: purplish | ruby | red | garnet | brick | brown
ROSÉ: pink | salmon | orange | copper

CLARITY:
clear | slight haze | cloudy

AROMA INTENSITY:
low | moderate | aromatic | powerful

DEVELOPMENT:
youthful | some age | aged

AROMAS:

DRY/SWEET:
bone dry | dry | off dry | medium sweet | sweet | very sweet

BODY:
very light | light | medium | medium-full | full-bodied | heavy

ACIDITY:
tart | crisp | fresh | smooth | flabby

TANNINS (IF PRESENT):
LEVEL: low | medium | high   TYPE: soft | round | dry | hard

BALANCE:
good | fair | unbalanced (excess: alcohol - acid - tannin - sugar)

FLAVOR INTENSITY:
low | moderate | flavorful | powerful

FLAVORS:

FINISH:
short (< 3 sec) | medium (4-5) | long (5-7) | v. long (>8 sec)

CONCLUSION:

STYLE:
traditional | in-between | modern

rating: ☆ ☆ ☆ ☆ ☆

FOOD: **FOOD PAIRING:**
                  MATCH: perfect | good | neutral | bad

tasting date: location:

tasting partner(s):

wine name:

producer:

region/appellation:

grape varieties:

vintage: alcohol: price:

COLOR DEPTH:
watery | pale | medium | deep | dark

COLOR HUE:
WHITE: greenish | yellow | straw yellow | gold | amber
RED: purplish | ruby | red | garnet | brick | brown
ROSÉ: pink | salmon | orange | copper

CLARITY:
clear | slight haze | cloudy

AROMA INTENSITY:
low | moderate | aromatic | powerful

DEVELOPMENT:
youthful | some age | aged

AROMAS:

DRY/SWEET:
bone dry | dry | off dry | medium sweet | sweet | very sweet

BODY:
very light | light | medium | medium-full | full-bodied | heavy

ACIDITY:
tart | crisp | fresh | smooth | flabby

TANNINS (IF PRESENT):
LEVEL: low | medium | high   TYPE: soft | round | dry | hard

BALANCE:
good | fair | unbalanced (excess: alcohol - acid - tannin - sugar)

FLAVOR INTENSITY:
low | moderate | flavorful | powerful

FLAVORS:

FINISH:
short (< 3 sec) | medium (4-5) | long (5-7) | v. long (>8 sec)

CONCLUSION:

STYLE:
traditional | in-between | modern

rating: ☆ ☆ ☆ ☆ ☆

FOOD: ### FOOD PAIRING:
              MATCH: perfect | good | neutral | bad

tasting date: location:

tasting partner(s):

wine name:

producer:

region/appellation:

grape varieties:

vintage: alcohol: price:

 COLOR DEPTH:
watery | pale | medium | deep | dark

COLOR HUE:
WHITE: greenish | yellow | straw yellow | gold | amber
RED: purplish | ruby | red | garnet | brick | brown
ROSÉ: pink | salmon | orange | copper

CLARITY:
clear | slight haze | cloudy

 AROMA INTENSITY:
low | moderate | aromatic | powerful

DEVELOPMENT:
youthful | some age | aged

AROMAS:

DRY/SWEET:
bone dry | dry | off dry | medium sweet | sweet | very sweet

BODY:
very light | light | medium | medium-full | full-bodied | heavy

ACIDITY:
tart | crisp | fresh | smooth | flabby

TANNINS (IF PRESENT):
LEVEL: low | medium | high   TYPE: soft | round | dry | hard

BALANCE:
good | fair | unbalanced (excess: alcohol - acid - tannin - sugar)

FLAVOR INTENSITY:
low | moderate | flavorful | powerful

FLAVORS:

FINISH:
short (< 3 sec) | medium (4-5) | long (5-7) | v. long (>8 sec)

CONCLUSION:

STYLE:
traditional | in-between | modern

rating: ☆ ☆ ☆ ☆ ☆

FOOD: **FOOD PAIRING:**
MATCH: perfect | good | neutral | bad

tasting date: location:

tasting partner(s):

wine name:

producer:

region/appellation:

grape varieties:

vintage: alcohol: price:

COLOR DEPTH:
watery | pale | medium | deep | dark

COLOR HUE:
WHITE: greenish | yellow | straw yellow | gold | amber
RED: purplish | ruby | red | garnet | brick | brown
ROSÉ: pink | salmon | orange | copper

CLARITY:
clear | slight haze | cloudy

AROMA INTENSITY:
low | moderate | aromatic | powerful

DEVELOPMENT:
youthful | some age | aged

AROMAS:

DRY/SWEET:
bone dry | dry | off dry | medium sweet | sweet | very sweet

BODY:
very light | light | medium | medium-full | full-bodied | heavy

ACIDITY:
tart | crisp | fresh | smooth | flabby

TANNINS (IF PRESENT):
LEVEL: low | medium | high   TYPE: soft | round | dry | hard

BALANCE:
good | fair | unbalanced (excess: alcohol - acid - tannin - sugar)

FLAVOR INTENSITY:
low | moderate | flavorful | powerful

FLAVORS:

FINISH:
short (< 3 sec) | medium (4-5) | long (5-7) | v. long (>8 sec)

CONCLUSION:

STYLE:
traditional | in-between | modern

rating: ☆ ☆ ☆ ☆ ☆

FOOD: **FOOD PAIRING:**
                MATCH: perfect | good | neutral | bad

tasting date: location:

tasting partner(s):

wine name:

producer:

region/appellation:

grape varieties:

vintage: alcohol: price:

 COLOR DEPTH:
watery | pale | medium | deep | dark

COLOR HUE:
WHITE: greenish | yellow | straw yellow | gold | amber
RED: purplish | ruby | red | garnet | brick | brown
ROSÉ: pink | salmon | orange | copper

CLARITY:
clear | slight haze | cloudy

 AROMA INTENSITY:
low | moderate | aromatic | powerful

DEVELOPMENT:
youthful | some age | aged

AROMAS:

 DRY/SWEET:
bone dry | dry | off dry | medium sweet | sweet | very sweet

BODY:
very light | light | medium | medium-full | full-bodied | heavy

ACIDITY:
tart | crisp | fresh | smooth | flabby

TANNINS (IF PRESENT):
LEVEL: low | medium | high   TYPE: soft | round | dry | hard

BALANCE:
good | fair | unbalanced (excess: alcohol - acid - tannin - sugar)

FLAVOR INTENSITY:
low | moderate | flavorful | powerful

FLAVORS:

FINISH:
short (< 3 sec) | medium (4-5) | long (5-7) | v. long (>8 sec)

CONCLUSION:

STYLE:
traditional | in-between | modern

rating: ☆ ☆ ☆ ☆ ☆

FOOD: **FOOD PAIRING:**
MATCH: perfect | good | neutral | bad

tasting date: location:

tasting partner(s):

wine name:

producer:

region/appellation:

grape varieties:

vintage: . alcohol: price:

COLOR DEPTH:
watery | pale | medium | deep | dark

COLOR HUE:
WHITE: greenish | yellow | straw yellow | gold | amber
RED: purplish | ruby | red | garnet | brick | brown
ROSÉ: pink | salmon | orange | copper

CLARITY:
clear | slight haze | cloudy

AROMA INTENSITY:
low | moderate | aromatic | powerful

DEVELOPMENT:
youthful | some age | aged

AROMAS:

DRY/SWEET:
bone dry | dry | off dry | medium sweet | sweet | very sweet

BODY:
very light | light | medium | medium-full | full-bodied | heavy

ACIDITY:
tart | crisp | fresh | smooth | flabby

TANNINS (IF PRESENT):
LEVEL: low | medium | high   TYPE: soft | round | dry | hard

BALANCE:
good | fair | unbalanced (excess: alcohol - acid - tannin - sugar)

FLAVOR INTENSITY:
low | moderate | flavorful | powerful

FLAVORS:

FINISH:
short (< 3 sec) | medium (4-5) | long (5-7) | v. long (>8 sec)

CONCLUSION:

STYLE:
traditional | in-between | modern

rating: ☆ ☆ ☆ ☆ ☆

FOOD: **FOOD PAIRING:**
MATCH: perfect | good | neutral | bad

tasting date: location:

tasting partner(s):

wine name:

producer:

region/appellation:

grape varieties:

vintage: alcohol: price:

COLOR DEPTH:
watery | pale | medium | deep | dark

COLOR HUE:
WHITE: greenish | yellow | straw yellow | gold | amber
RED: purplish | ruby | red | garnet | brick | brown
ROSÉ: pink | salmon | orange | copper

CLARITY:
clear | slight haze | cloudy

AROMA INTENSITY:
low | moderate | aromatic | powerful

DEVELOPMENT:
youthful | some age | aged

AROMAS:

DRY/SWEET:
bone dry | dry | off dry | medium sweet | sweet | very sweet

BODY:
very light | light | medium | medium-full | full-bodied | heavy

ACIDITY:
tart | crisp | fresh | smooth | flabby

TANNINS (IF PRESENT):
LEVEL: low | medium | high   TYPE: soft | round | dry | hard

BALANCE:
good | fair | unbalanced (excess: alcohol - acid - tannin - sugar)

FLAVOR INTENSITY:
low | moderate | flavorful | powerful

FLAVORS:

FINISH:
short (< 3 sec) | medium (4-5) | long (5-7) | v. long (>8 sec)

CONCLUSION:

STYLE:
traditional | in-between | modern

rating: ☆ ☆ ☆ ☆ ☆

FOOD: **FOOD PAIRING:**

MATCH: perfect | good | neutral | bad

tasting date: location:

tasting partner(s):

wine name:

producer:

region/appellation:

grape varieties:

vintage: alcohol: price:

COLOR DEPTH:
watery | pale | medium | deep | dark

COLOR HUE:
WHITE: greenish | yellow | straw yellow | gold | amber
RED: purplish | ruby | red | garnet | brick | brown
ROSÉ: pink | salmon | orange | copper

CLARITY:
clear | slight haze | cloudy

AROMA INTENSITY:
low | moderate | aromatic | powerful

DEVELOPMENT:
youthful | some age | aged

AROMAS:

DRY/SWEET:
bone dry | dry | off dry | medium sweet | sweet | very sweet

BODY:
very light | light | medium | medium-full | full-bodied | heavy

ACIDITY:
tart | crisp | fresh | smooth | flabby

TANNINS (IF PRESENT):
LEVEL: low | medium | high   TYPE: soft | round | dry | hard

BALANCE:
good | fair | unbalanced (excess: alcohol - acid - tannin - sugar)

FLAVOR INTENSITY:
low | moderate | flavorful | powerful

FLAVORS:

FINISH:
short (< 3 sec) | medium (4-5) | long (5-7) | v. long (>8 sec)

CONCLUSION:

STYLE:
traditional | in-between | modern

rating: ☆ ☆ ☆ ☆ ☆

FOOD: **FOOD PAIRING:**

         MATCH: perfect | good | neutral | bad

tasting date: location:

tasting partner(s):

wine name:

producer:

region/appellation:

grape varieties:

vintage: alcohol: price:

COLOR DEPTH:
watery | pale | medium | deep | dark

COLOR HUE:
WHITE: greenish | yellow | straw yellow | gold | amber
RED: purplish | ruby | red | garnet | brick | brown
ROSÉ: pink | salmon | orange | copper

CLARITY:
clear | slight haze | cloudy

AROMA INTENSITY:
low | moderate | aromatic | powerful

DEVELOPMENT:
youthful | some age | aged

AROMAS:

DRY/SWEET:
bone dry | dry | off dry | medium sweet | sweet | very sweet

BODY:
very light | light | medium | medium-full | full-bodied | heavy

ACIDITY:
tart | crisp | fresh | smooth | flabby

TANNINS (IF PRESENT):
LEVEL: low | medium | high   TYPE: soft | round | dry | hard

BALANCE:
good | fair | unbalanced (excess: alcohol - acid - tannin - sugar)

FLAVOR INTENSITY:
low | moderate | flavorful | powerful

FLAVORS:

FINISH:
short (< 3 sec) | medium (4-5) | long (5-7) | v. long (>8 sec)

CONCLUSION:

STYLE:
traditional | in-between | modern

rating: ☆ ☆ ☆ ☆ ☆

FOOD: **FOOD PAIRING:**

MATCH: perfect | good | neutral | bad

tasting date: location:

tasting partner(s):

wine name:

producer:

region/appellation:

grape varieties:

vintage: alcohol: price:

COLOR DEPTH:
watery | pale | medium | deep | dark

COLOR HUE:
WHITE: greenish | yellow | straw yellow | gold | amber
RED: purplish | ruby | red | garnet | brick | brown
ROSÉ: pink | salmon | orange | copper

CLARITY:
clear | slight haze | cloudy

AROMA INTENSITY:
low | moderate | aromatic | powerful

DEVELOPMENT:
youthful | some age | aged

AROMAS:

DRY/SWEET:
bone dry | dry | off dry | medium sweet | sweet | very sweet

BODY:
very light | light | medium | medium-full | full-bodied | heavy

ACIDITY:
tart | crisp | fresh | smooth | flabby

TANNINS (IF PRESENT):
LEVEL: low | medium | high   TYPE: soft | round | dry | hard

BALANCE:
good | fair | unbalanced (excess: alcohol - acid - tannin - sugar)

FLAVOR INTENSITY:
low | moderate | flavorful | powerful

FLAVORS:

FINISH:
short (< 3 sec) | medium (4-5) | long (5-7) | v. long (>8 sec)

CONCLUSION:

STYLE:
traditional | in-between | modern

rating: ☆ ☆ ☆ ☆ ☆

FOOD: **FOOD PAIRING:**

                MATCH: perfect | good | neutral | bad

tasting date: location:

tasting partner(s):

wine name:

producer:

region/appellation:

grape varieties:

vintage: alcohol: price:

 COLOR DEPTH:
watery | pale | medium | deep | dark

COLOR HUE:
WHITE: greenish | yellow | straw yellow | gold | amber
RED: purplish | ruby | red | garnet | brick | brown
ROSÉ: pink | salmon | orange | copper

CLARITY:
clear | slight haze | cloudy

AROMA INTENSITY:
low | moderate | aromatic | powerful

DEVELOPMENT:
youthful | some age | aged

AROMAS:

 DRY/SWEET:
bone dry | dry | off dry | medium sweet | sweet | very sweet

BODY:
very light | light | medium | medium-full | full-bodied | heavy

ACIDITY:
tart | crisp | fresh | smooth | flabby

TANNINS (IF PRESENT):
LEVEL: low | medium | high   TYPE: soft | round | dry | hard

BALANCE:
good | fair | unbalanced (excess: alcohol - acid - tannin - sugar)

FLAVOR INTENSITY:
low | moderate | flavorful | powerful

FLAVORS:

FINISH:
short (< 3 sec) | medium (4-5) | long (5-7) | v. long (>8 sec)

CONCLUSION:

STYLE:
traditional | in-between | modern

rating: ☆ ☆ ☆ ☆ ☆

FOOD: **FOOD PAIRING:**
                    MATCH: perfect | good | neutral | bad

tasting date: location:

tasting partner(s):

wine name:

producer:

region/appellation:

grape varieties:

vintage: alcohol: price:

COLOR DEPTH:
watery | pale | medium | deep | dark

COLOR HUE:
WHITE: greenish | yellow | straw yellow | gold | amber
RED: purplish | ruby | red | garnet | brick | brown
ROSÉ: pink | salmon | orange | copper

CLARITY:
clear | slight haze | cloudy

AROMA INTENSITY:
low | moderate | aromatic | powerful

DEVELOPMENT:
youthful | some age | aged

AROMAS:

DRY/SWEET:
bone dry | dry | off dry | medium sweet | sweet | very sweet

BODY:
very light | light | medium | medium-full | full-bodied | heavy

ACIDITY:
tart | crisp | fresh | smooth | flabby

TANNINS (IF PRESENT):
LEVEL: low | medium | high   TYPE: soft | round | dry | hard

BALANCE:
good | fair | unbalanced (excess: alcohol - acid - tannin - sugar)

FLAVOR INTENSITY:
low | moderate | flavorful | powerful

FLAVORS:

FINISH:
short (< 3 sec) | medium (4-5) | long (5-7) | v. long (>8 sec)

CONCLUSION:

STYLE:
traditional | in-between | modern

rating: ☆ ☆ ☆ ☆ ☆

FOOD:

FOOD PAIRING:
MATCH: perfect | good | neutral | bad

tasting date: location:

tasting partner(s):

wine name:

producer:

region/appellation:

grape varieties:

vintage: alcohol: price:

COLOR DEPTH:
watery | pale | medium | deep | dark

COLOR HUE:
WHITE: greenish | yellow | straw yellow | gold | amber
RED: purplish | ruby | red | garnet | brick | brown
ROSÉ: pink | salmon | orange | copper

CLARITY:
clear | slight haze | cloudy

AROMA INTENSITY:
low | moderate | aromatic | powerful

DEVELOPMENT:
youthful | some age | aged

AROMAS:

DRY/SWEET:
bone dry | dry | off dry | medium sweet | sweet | very sweet

BODY:
very light | light | medium | medium-full | full-bodied | heavy

ACIDITY:
tart | crisp | fresh | smooth | flabby

TANNINS (IF PRESENT):
LEVEL: low | medium | high   TYPE: soft | round | dry | hard

BALANCE:
good | fair | unbalanced (excess: alcohol - acid - tannin - sugar)

FLAVOR INTENSITY:
low | moderate | flavorful | powerful

FLAVORS:

FINISH:
short (< 3 sec) | medium (4-5) | long (5-7) | v. long (>8 sec)

CONCLUSION:

STYLE:
traditional | in-between | modern

rating: ☆ ☆ ☆ ☆ ☆

FOOD: **FOOD PAIRING:**
                  MATCH: perfect | good | neutral | bad

tasting date: location:

tasting partner(s):

wine name:

producer:

region/appellation:

grape varieties:

vintage: alcohol: price:

COLOR DEPTH:
watery | pale | medium | deep | dark

COLOR HUE:
WHITE: greenish | yellow | straw yellow | gold | amber
RED: purplish | ruby | red | garnet | brick | brown
ROSÉ: pink | salmon | orange | copper

CLARITY:
clear | slight haze | cloudy

AROMA INTENSITY:
low | moderate | aromatic | powerful

DEVELOPMENT:
youthful | some age | aged

AROMAS:

DRY/SWEET:
bone dry | dry | off dry | medium sweet | sweet | very sweet

BODY:
very light | light | medium | medium-full | full-bodied | heavy

ACIDITY:
tart | crisp | fresh | smooth | flabby

TANNINS (IF PRESENT):
LEVEL: low | medium | high   TYPE: soft | round | dry | hard

BALANCE:
good | fair | unbalanced (excess: alcohol - acid - tannin - sugar)

FLAVOR INTENSITY:
low | moderate | flavorful | powerful

FLAVORS:

FINISH:
short (< 3 sec) | medium (4-5) | long (5-7) | v. long (>8 sec)

CONCLUSION:

STYLE:
traditional | in-between | modern

rating: ☆ ☆ ☆ ☆ ☆

FOOD: **FOOD PAIRING:**
                    MATCH: perfect | good | neutral | bad

tasting date: location:

tasting partner(s):

wine name:

producer:

region/appellation:

grape varieties:

vintage: alcohol: price:

COLOR DEPTH:
watery | pale | medium | deep | dark

COLOR HUE:
WHITE: greenish | yellow | straw yellow | gold | amber
RED: purplish | ruby | red | garnet | brick | brown
ROSÉ: pink | salmon | orange | copper

CLARITY:
clear | slight haze | cloudy

AROMA INTENSITY:
low | moderate | aromatic | powerful

DEVELOPMENT:
youthful | some age | aged

AROMAS:

DRY/SWEET:
bone dry | dry | off dry | medium sweet | sweet | very sweet

BODY:
very light | light | medium | medium-full | full-bodied | heavy

ACIDITY:
tart | crisp | fresh | smooth | flabby

TANNINS (IF PRESENT):
LEVEL: low | medium | high   TYPE: soft | round | dry | hard

BALANCE:
good | fair | unbalanced (excess: alcohol - acid - tannin - sugar)

FLAVOR INTENSITY:
low | moderate | flavorful | powerful

FLAVORS:

FINISH:
short (< 3 sec) | medium (4-5) | long (5-7) | v. long (>8 sec)

CONCLUSION:

STYLE:
traditional | in-between | modern

rating: ☆ ☆ ☆ ☆ ☆

FOOD: **FOOD PAIRING:**
                    MATCH: perfect | good | neutral | bad

tasting date: location:

tasting partner(s):

wine name:

producer:

region/appellation:

grape varieties:

vintage: alcohol: price:

COLOR DEPTH:
watery | pale | medium | deep | dark

COLOR HUE:
WHITE: greenish | yellow | straw yellow | gold | amber
RED: purplish | ruby | red | garnet | brick | brown
ROSÉ: pink | salmon | orange | copper

CLARITY:
clear | slight haze | cloudy

AROMA INTENSITY:
low | moderate | aromatic | powerful

DEVELOPMENT:
youthful | some age | aged

AROMAS:

DRY/SWEET:
bone dry | dry | off dry | medium sweet | sweet | very sweet

BODY:
very light | light | medium | medium-full | full-bodied | heavy

ACIDITY:
tart | crisp | fresh | smooth | flabby

TANNINS (IF PRESENT):
LEVEL: low | medium | high   TYPE: soft | round | dry | hard

BALANCE:
good | fair | unbalanced (excess: alcohol - acid - tannin - sugar)

FLAVOR INTENSITY:
low | moderate | flavorful | powerful

FLAVORS:

FINISH:
short (< 3 sec) | medium (4-5) | long (5-7) | v. long (>8 sec)

CONCLUSION:

STYLE:
traditional | in-between | modern

rating: ☆ ☆ ☆ ☆ ☆

FOOD: **FOOD PAIRING:**
                    MATCH: perfect | good | neutral | bad

tasting date: location:

tasting partner(s):

wine name:

producer:

region/appellation:

grape varieties:

vintage: alcohol: price:

COLOR DEPTH:
watery | pale | medium | deep | dark

COLOR HUE:
WHITE: greenish | yellow | straw yellow | gold | amber
RED: purplish | ruby | red | garnet | brick | brown
ROSÉ: pink | salmon | orange | copper

CLARITY:
clear | slight haze | cloudy

AROMA INTENSITY:
low | moderate | aromatic | powerful

DEVELOPMENT:
youthful | some age | aged

AROMAS:

DRY/SWEET:
bone dry | dry | off dry | medium sweet | sweet | very sweet

BODY:
very light | light | medium | medium-full | full-bodied | heavy

ACIDITY:
tart | crisp | fresh | smooth | flabby

TANNINS (IF PRESENT):
LEVEL: low | medium | high   TYPE: soft | round | dry | hard

BALANCE:
good | fair | unbalanced (excess: alcohol - acid - tannin - sugar)

FLAVOR INTENSITY:
low | moderate | flavorful | powerful

FLAVORS:

FINISH:
short (< 3 sec) | medium (4-5) | long (5-7) | v. long (>8 sec)

CONCLUSION:

STYLE:
traditional | in-between | modern

rating: ☆ ☆ ☆ ☆ ☆

FOOD: **FOOD PAIRING:**

MATCH: perfect | good | neutral | bad

tasting date: location:

tasting partner(s):

wine name:

producer:

region/appellation:

grape varieties:

vintage: alcohol: price:

COLOR DEPTH:
watery | pale | medium | deep | dark

COLOR HUE:
WHITE: greenish | yellow | straw yellow | gold | amber
RED: purplish | ruby | red | garnet | brick | brown
ROSÉ: pink | salmon | orange | copper

CLARITY:
clear | slight haze | cloudy

AROMA INTENSITY:
low | moderate | aromatic | powerful

DEVELOPMENT:
youthful | some age | aged

AROMAS:

DRY/SWEET:
bone dry | dry | off dry | medium sweet | sweet | very sweet

BODY:
very light | light | medium | medium-full | full-bodied | heavy

ACIDITY:
tart | crisp | fresh | smooth | flabby

TANNINS (IF PRESENT):
LEVEL: low | medium | high   TYPE: soft | round | dry | hard

BALANCE:
good | fair | unbalanced (excess: alcohol - acid - tannin - sugar)

FLAVOR INTENSITY:
low | moderate | flavorful | powerful

FLAVORS:

FINISH:
short (< 3 sec) | medium (4-5) | long (5-7) | v. long (>8 sec)

CONCLUSION:

STYLE:
traditional | in-between | modern

rating: ☆ ☆ ☆ ☆ ☆

FOOD: **FOOD PAIRING:**

                     MATCH: perfect | good | neutral | bad

tasting date: location:

tasting partner(s):

wine name:

producer:

region/appellation:

grape varieties:

vintage: alcohol: price:

COLOR DEPTH:
watery | pale | medium | deep | dark

COLOR HUE:
WHITE: greenish | yellow | straw yellow | gold | amber
RED: purplish | ruby | red | garnet | brick | brown
ROSÉ: pink | salmon | orange | copper

CLARITY:
clear | slight haze | cloudy

AROMA INTENSITY:
low | moderate | aromatic | powerful

DEVELOPMENT:
youthful | some age | aged

AROMAS:

DRY/SWEET:
bone dry | dry | off dry | medium sweet | sweet | very sweet

BODY:
very light | light | medium | medium-full | full-bodied | heavy

ACIDITY:
tart | crisp | fresh | smooth | flabby

TANNINS (IF PRESENT):
LEVEL: low | medium | high   TYPE: soft | round | dry | hard

BALANCE:
good | fair | unbalanced (excess: alcohol - acid - tannin - sugar)

FLAVOR INTENSITY:
low | moderate | flavorful | powerful

FLAVORS:

FINISH:
short (< 3 sec) | medium (4-5) | long (5-7) | v. long (>8 sec)

CONCLUSION:

STYLE:
traditional | in-between | modern

rating: ☆ ☆ ☆ ☆ ☆

FOOD: **FOOD PAIRING:**
                MATCH: perfect | good | neutral | bad

tasting date: location:

tasting partner(s):

wine name:

producer:

region/appellation:

grape varieties:

vintage: alcohol: price:

COLOR DEPTH:
watery | pale | medium | deep | dark
COLOR HUE:
WHITE: greenish | yellow | straw yellow | gold | amber
RED: purplish | ruby | red | garnet | brick | brown
ROSÉ: pink | salmon | orange | copper
CLARITY:
clear | slight haze | cloudy

AROMA INTENSITY:
low | moderate | aromatic | powerful
DEVELOPMENT:
youthful | some age | aged
AROMAS:

DRY/SWEET:
bone dry | dry | off dry | medium sweet | sweet | very sweet
BODY:
very light | light | medium | medium-full | full-bodied | heavy
ACIDITY:
tart | crisp | fresh | smooth | flabby
TANNINS (IF PRESENT):
LEVEL: low | medium | high   TYPE: soft | round | dry | hard
BALANCE:
good | fair | unbalanced (excess: alcohol - acid - tannin - sugar)
FLAVOR INTENSITY:
low | moderate | flavorful | powerful
FLAVORS:

FINISH:
short (< 3 sec) | medium (4-5) | long (5-7) | v. long (>8 sec)
CONCLUSION:

STYLE:
traditional | in-between | modern

rating: ☆ ☆ ☆ ☆ ☆

FOOD: **FOOD PAIRING:**
                MATCH: perfect | good | neutral | bad

tasting date: location:

tasting partner(s):

wine name:

producer:

region/appellation:

grape varieties:

vintage: alcohol: price:

COLOR DEPTH:
watery | pale | medium | deep | dark

COLOR HUE:
WHITE: greenish | yellow | straw yellow | gold | amber
RED: purplish | ruby | red | garnet | brick | brown
ROSÉ: pink | salmon | orange | copper

CLARITY:
clear | slight haze | cloudy

AROMA INTENSITY:
low | moderate | aromatic | powerful

DEVELOPMENT:
youthful | some age | aged

AROMAS:

DRY/SWEET:
bone dry | dry | off dry | medium sweet | sweet | very sweet

BODY:
very light | light | medium | medium-full | full-bodied | heavy

ACIDITY:
tart | crisp | fresh | smooth | flabby

TANNINS (IF PRESENT):
LEVEL: low | medium | high   TYPE: soft | round | dry | hard

BALANCE:
good | fair | unbalanced (excess: alcohol - acid - tannin - sugar)

FLAVOR INTENSITY:
low | moderate | flavorful | powerful

FLAVORS:

FINISH:
short (< 3 sec) | medium (4-5) | long (5-7) | v. long (>8 sec)

CONCLUSION:

STYLE:
traditional | in-between | modern

rating: ☆ ☆ ☆ ☆ ☆

FOOD: **FOOD PAIRING:**
                    MATCH: perfect | good | neutral | bad

tasting date: location:

tasting partner(s):

wine name:

producer:

region/appellation:

grape varieties:

vintage: alcohol: price:

COLOR DEPTH:
watery | pale | medium | deep | dark

COLOR HUE:
WHITE: greenish | yellow | straw yellow | gold | amber
RED: purplish | ruby | red | garnet | brick | brown
ROSÉ: pink | salmon | orange | copper

CLARITY:
clear | slight haze | cloudy

AROMA INTENSITY:
low | moderate | aromatic | powerful

DEVELOPMENT:
youthful | some age | aged

AROMAS:

DRY/SWEET:
bone dry | dry | off dry | medium sweet | sweet | very sweet

BODY:
very light | light | medium | medium-full | full-bodied | heavy

ACIDITY:
tart | crisp | fresh | smooth | flabby

TANNINS (IF PRESENT):
LEVEL: low | medium | high   TYPE: soft | round | dry | hard

BALANCE:
good | fair | unbalanced (excess: alcohol - acid - tannin - sugar)

FLAVOR INTENSITY:
low | moderate | flavorful | powerful

FLAVORS:

FINISH:
short (< 3 sec) | medium (4-5) | long (5-7) | v. long (>8 sec)

CONCLUSION:

STYLE:
traditional | in-between | modern

rating: ☆ ☆ ☆ ☆ ☆

FOOD: ### FOOD PAIRING:
MATCH: perfect | good | neutral | bad

tasting date: location:

tasting partner(s):

wine name:

producer:

region/appellation:

grape varieties:

vintage: alcohol: price:

 ### COLOR DEPTH:
watery | pale | medium | deep | dark

COLOR HUE:
WHITE: greenish | yellow | straw yellow | gold | amber
RED: purplish | ruby | red | garnet | brick | brown
ROSÉ: pink | salmon | orange | copper

CLARITY:
clear | slight haze | cloudy

 ### AROMA INTENSITY:
low | moderate | aromatic | powerful

DEVELOPMENT:
youthful | some age | aged

AROMAS:

 ### DRY/SWEET:
bone dry | dry | off dry | medium sweet | sweet | very sweet

BODY:
very light | light | medium | medium-full | full-bodied | heavy

ACIDITY:
tart | crisp | fresh | smooth | flabby

TANNINS (IF PRESENT):
LEVEL: low | medium | high   TYPE: soft | round | dry | hard

BALANCE:
good | fair | unbalanced (excess: alcohol - acid - tannin - sugar)

FLAVOR INTENSITY:
low | moderate | flavorful | powerful

FLAVORS:

FINISH:
short (< 3 sec) | medium (4-5) | long (5-7) | v. long (>8 sec)

CONCLUSION:

STYLE:
traditional | in-between | modern

rating: ☆ ☆ ☆ ☆ ☆

FOOD: **FOOD PAIRING:**
MATCH: perfect | good | neutral | bad

tasting date: location:

tasting partner(s):

wine name:

producer:

region/appellation:

grape varieties:

vintage: alcohol: price:

COLOR DEPTH:
watery | pale | medium | deep | dark

COLOR HUE:
WHITE: greenish | yellow | straw yellow | gold | amber
RED: purplish | ruby | red | garnet | brick | brown
ROSÉ: pink | salmon | orange | copper

CLARITY:
clear | slight haze | cloudy

AROMA INTENSITY:
low | moderate | aromatic | powerful

DEVELOPMENT:
youthful | some age | aged

AROMAS:

DRY/SWEET:
bone dry | dry | off dry | medium sweet | sweet | very sweet

BODY:
very light | light | medium | medium-full | full-bodied | heavy

ACIDITY:
tart | crisp | fresh | smooth | flabby

TANNINS (IF PRESENT):
LEVEL: low | medium | high   TYPE: soft | round | dry | hard

BALANCE:
good | fair | unbalanced (excess: alcohol - acid - tannin - sugar)

FLAVOR INTENSITY:
low | moderate | flavorful | powerful

FLAVORS:

FINISH:
short (< 3 sec) | medium (4-5) | long (5-7) | v. long (>8 sec)

CONCLUSION:

STYLE:
traditional | in-between | modern

rating: ☆ ☆ ☆ ☆ ☆

FOOD: **FOOD PAIRING:**
                    MATCH: perfect | good | neutral | bad

tasting date: location:

tasting partner(s):

wine name:

producer:

region/appellation:

grape varieties:

vintage: alcohol: price:

COLOR DEPTH:
watery | pale | medium | deep | dark

COLOR HUE:
WHITE: greenish | yellow | straw yellow | gold | amber
RED: purplish | ruby | red | garnet | brick | brown
ROSÉ: pink | salmon | orange | copper

CLARITY:
clear | slight haze | cloudy

AROMA INTENSITY:
low | moderate | aromatic | powerful

DEVELOPMENT:
youthful | some age | aged

AROMAS:

DRY/SWEET:
bone dry | dry | off dry | medium sweet | sweet | very sweet

BODY:
very light | light | medium | medium-full | full-bodied | heavy

ACIDITY:
tart | crisp | fresh | smooth | flabby

TANNINS (IF PRESENT):
LEVEL: low | medium | high   TYPE: soft | round | dry | hard

BALANCE:
good | fair | unbalanced (excess: alcohol - acid - tannin - sugar)

FLAVOR INTENSITY:
low | moderate | flavorful | powerful

FLAVORS:

FINISH:
short (< 3 sec) | medium (4-5) | long (5-7) | v. long (>8 sec)

CONCLUSION:

STYLE:
traditional | in-between | modern

rating: ☆ ☆ ☆ ☆ ☆

FOOD: **FOOD PAIRING:**

MATCH: perfect | good | neutral | bad

tasting date: location:

tasting partner(s):

wine name:

producer:

region/appellation:

grape varieties:

vintage: alcohol: price:

COLOR DEPTH:
watery | pale | medium | deep | dark

COLOR HUE:
WHITE: greenish | yellow | straw yellow | gold | amber
RED: purplish | ruby | red | garnet | brick | brown
ROSÉ: pink | salmon | orange | copper

CLARITY:
clear | slight haze | cloudy

AROMA INTENSITY:
low | moderate | aromatic | powerful

DEVELOPMENT:
youthful | some age | aged

AROMAS:

DRY/SWEET:
bone dry | dry | off dry | medium sweet | sweet | very sweet

BODY:
very light | light | medium | medium-full | full-bodied | heavy

ACIDITY:
tart | crisp | fresh | smooth | flabby

TANNINS (IF PRESENT):
LEVEL: low | medium | high   TYPE: soft | round | dry | hard

BALANCE:
good | fair | unbalanced (excess: alcohol - acid - tannin - sugar)

FLAVOR INTENSITY:
low | moderate | flavorful | powerful

FLAVORS:

FINISH:
short (< 3 sec) | medium (4-5) | long (5-7) | v. long (>8 sec)

CONCLUSION:

STYLE:
traditional | in-between | modern

rating: ☆ ☆ ☆ ☆ ☆

FOOD: **FOOD PAIRING:**
               MATCH: perfect | good | neutral | bad

tasting date: location:

tasting partner(s):

wine name:

producer:

region/appellation:

grape varieties:

vintage: alcohol: price:

 COLOR DEPTH:
watery | pale | medium | deep | dark

COLOR HUE:
WHITE: greenish | yellow | straw yellow | gold | amber
RED: purplish | ruby | red | garnet | brick | brown
ROSÉ: pink | salmon | orange | copper

CLARITY:
clear | slight haze | cloudy

AROMA INTENSITY:
low | moderate | aromatic | powerful

DEVELOPMENT:
youthful | some age | aged

AROMAS:

 DRY/SWEET:
bone dry | dry | off dry | medium sweet | sweet | very sweet

BODY:
very light | light | medium | medium-full | full-bodied | heavy

ACIDITY:
tart | crisp | fresh | smooth | flabby

TANNINS (IF PRESENT):
LEVEL: low | medium | high   TYPE: soft | round | dry | hard

BALANCE:
good | fair | unbalanced (excess: alcohol - acid - tannin - sugar)

FLAVOR INTENSITY:
low | moderate | flavorful | powerful

FLAVORS:

FINISH:
short (< 3 sec) | medium (4-5) | long (5-7) | v. long (>8 sec)

CONCLUSION:

STYLE:
traditional | in-between | modern

rating: ☆ ☆ ☆ ☆ ☆

FOOD: **FOOD PAIRING:**
MATCH: perfect | good | neutral | bad

tasting date: location:

tasting partner(s):

wine name:

producer:

region/appellation:

grape varieties:

vintage: alcohol: price:

COLOR DEPTH:
watery | pale | medium | deep | dark

COLOR HUE:
WHITE: greenish | yellow | straw yellow | gold | amber
RED: purplish | ruby | red | garnet | brick | brown
ROSÉ: pink | salmon | orange | copper

CLARITY:
clear | slight haze | cloudy

AROMA INTENSITY:
low | moderate | aromatic | powerful

DEVELOPMENT:
youthful | some age | aged

AROMAS:

DRY/SWEET:
bone dry | dry | off dry | medium sweet | sweet | very sweet

BODY:
very light | light | medium | medium-full | full-bodied | heavy

ACIDITY:
tart | crisp | fresh | smooth | flabby

TANNINS (IF PRESENT):
LEVEL: low | medium | high   TYPE: soft | round | dry | hard

BALANCE:
good | fair | unbalanced (excess: alcohol - acid - tannin - sugar)

FLAVOR INTENSITY:
low | moderate | flavorful | powerful

FLAVORS:

FINISH:
short (< 3 sec) | medium (4-5) | long (5-7) | v. long (>8 sec)

CONCLUSION:

STYLE:
traditional | in-between | modern

rating: ☆ ☆ ☆ ☆ ☆

FOOD: **FOOD PAIRING:**

MATCH: perfect | good | neutral | bad

tasting date: location:

tasting partner(s):

wine name:

producer:

region/appellation:

grape varieties:

vintage: alcohol: price:

COLOR DEPTH:
watery | pale | medium | deep | dark

COLOR HUE:
WHITE: greenish | yellow | straw yellow | gold | amber
RED: purplish | ruby | red | garnet | brick | brown
ROSÉ: pink | salmon | orange | copper

CLARITY:
clear | slight haze | cloudy

AROMA INTENSITY:
low | moderate | aromatic | powerful

DEVELOPMENT:
youthful | some age | aged

AROMAS:

DRY/SWEET:
bone dry | dry | off dry | medium sweet | sweet | very sweet

BODY:
very light | light | medium | medium-full | full-bodied | heavy

ACIDITY:
tart | crisp | fresh | smooth | flabby

TANNINS (IF PRESENT):
LEVEL: low | medium | high   TYPE: soft | round | dry | hard

BALANCE:
good | fair | unbalanced (excess: alcohol - acid - tannin - sugar)

FLAVOR INTENSITY:
low | moderate | flavorful | powerful

FLAVORS:

FINISH:
short (< 3 sec) | medium (4-5) | long (5-7) | v. long (>8 sec)

CONCLUSION:

STYLE:
traditional | in-between | modern

rating: ☆ ☆ ☆ ☆ ☆

FOOD: **FOOD PAIRING:**

MATCH: perfect | good | neutral | bad

tasting date: location:

tasting partner(s):

wine name:

producer:

region/appellation:

grape varieties:

vintage: alcohol: price:

COLOR DEPTH:
watery | pale | medium | deep | dark

COLOR HUE:
WHITE: greenish | yellow | straw yellow | gold | amber
RED: purplish | ruby | red | garnet | brick | brown
ROSÉ: pink | salmon | orange | copper

CLARITY:
clear | slight haze | cloudy

AROMA INTENSITY:
low | moderate | aromatic | powerful

DEVELOPMENT:
youthful | some age | aged

AROMAS:

DRY/SWEET:
bone dry | dry | off dry | medium sweet | sweet | very sweet

BODY:
very light | light | medium | medium-full | full-bodied | heavy

ACIDITY:
tart | crisp | fresh | smooth | flabby

TANNINS (IF PRESENT):
LEVEL: low | medium | high   TYPE: soft | round | dry | hard

BALANCE:
good | fair | unbalanced (excess: alcohol - acid - tannin - sugar)

FLAVOR INTENSITY:
low | moderate | flavorful | powerful

FLAVORS:

FINISH:
short (< 3 sec) | medium (4-5) | long (5-7) | v. long (>8 sec)

CONCLUSION:

STYLE:
traditional | in-between | modern

rating: ☆ ☆ ☆ ☆ ☆

FOOD: **FOOD PAIRING:**
MATCH: perfect | good | neutral | bad

tasting date: location:

tasting partner(s):

wine name:

producer:

region/appellation:

grape varieties:

vintage: alcohol: price:

COLOR DEPTH:
watery | pale | medium | deep | dark

COLOR HUE:
WHITE: greenish | yellow | straw yellow | gold | amber
RED: purplish | ruby | red | garnet | brick | brown
ROSÉ: pink | salmon | orange | copper

CLARITY:
clear | slight haze | cloudy

AROMA INTENSITY:
low | moderate | aromatic | powerful

DEVELOPMENT:
youthful | some age | aged

AROMAS:

DRY/SWEET:
bone dry | dry | off dry | medium sweet | sweet | very sweet

BODY:
very light | light | medium | medium-full | full-bodied | heavy

ACIDITY:
tart | crisp | fresh | smooth | flabby

TANNINS (IF PRESENT):
LEVEL: low | medium | high   TYPE: soft | round | dry | hard

BALANCE:
good | fair | unbalanced (excess: alcohol - acid - tannin - sugar)

FLAVOR INTENSITY:
low | moderate | flavorful | powerful

FLAVORS:

FINISH:
short (< 3 sec) | medium (4-5) | long (5-7) | v. long (>8 sec)

CONCLUSION:

STYLE:
traditional | in-between | modern

rating: ☆ ☆ ☆ ☆ ☆

FOOD: ### FOOD PAIRING:
MATCH: perfect | good | neutral | bad

tasting date: location:

tasting partner(s):

wine name:

producer:

region/appellation:

grape varieties:

vintage: alcohol: price:

COLOR DEPTH:
watery | pale | medium | deep | dark

COLOR HUE:
WHITE: greenish | yellow | straw yellow | gold | amber
RED: purplish | ruby | red | garnet | brick | brown
ROSÉ: pink | salmon | orange | copper

CLARITY:
clear | slight haze | cloudy

AROMA INTENSITY:
low | moderate | aromatic | powerful

DEVELOPMENT:
youthful | some age | aged

AROMAS:

DRY/SWEET:
bone dry | dry | off dry | medium sweet | sweet | very sweet

BODY:
very light | light | medium | medium-full | full-bodied | heavy

ACIDITY:
tart | crisp | fresh | smooth | flabby

TANNINS (IF PRESENT):
LEVEL: low | medium | high   TYPE: soft | round | dry | hard

BALANCE:
good | fair | unbalanced (excess: alcohol - acid - tannin - sugar)

FLAVOR INTENSITY:
low | moderate | flavorful | powerful

FLAVORS:

FINISH:
short (< 3 sec) | medium (4-5) | long (5-7) | v. long (>8 sec)

CONCLUSION:

STYLE:
traditional | in-between | modern

rating: ☆ ☆ ☆ ☆ ☆

FOOD: **FOOD PAIRING:**
                         MATCH: perfect | good | neutral | bad

tasting date: location:

tasting partner(s):

wine name:

producer:

region/appellation:

grape varieties:

vintage: alcohol: price:

 COLOR DEPTH:
watery | pale | medium | deep | dark

COLOR HUE:
WHITE: greenish | yellow | straw yellow | gold | amber
RED: purplish | ruby | red | garnet | brick | brown
ROSÉ: pink | salmon | orange | copper

CLARITY:
clear | slight haze | cloudy

 AROMA INTENSITY:
low | moderate | aromatic | powerful

DEVELOPMENT:
youthful | some age | aged

AROMAS:

 DRY/SWEET:
bone dry | dry | off dry | medium sweet | sweet | very sweet

BODY:
very light | light | medium | medium-full | full-bodied | heavy

ACIDITY:
tart | crisp | fresh | smooth | flabby

TANNINS (IF PRESENT):
LEVEL: low | medium | high   TYPE: soft | round | dry | hard

BALANCE:
good | fair | unbalanced (excess: alcohol - acid - tannin - sugar)

FLAVOR INTENSITY:
low | moderate | flavorful | powerful

FLAVORS:

FINISH:
short (< 3 sec) | medium (4-5) | long (5-7) | v. long (>8 sec)

CONCLUSION:

STYLE:
traditional | in-between | modern

rating: ☆ ☆ ☆ ☆ ☆

FOOD: **FOOD PAIRING:**
                MATCH: perfect | good | neutral | bad

tasting date: location:

tasting partner(s):

wine name:

producer:

region/appellation:

grape varieties:

vintage: alcohol: price:

COLOR DEPTH:
watery | pale | medium | deep | dark

COLOR HUE:
WHITE: greenish | yellow | straw yellow | gold | amber
RED: purplish | ruby | red | garnet | brick | brown
ROSÉ: pink | salmon | orange | copper

CLARITY:
clear | slight haze | cloudy

AROMA INTENSITY:
low | moderate | aromatic | powerful

DEVELOPMENT:
youthful | some age | aged

AROMAS:

DRY/SWEET:
bone dry | dry | off dry | medium sweet | sweet | very sweet

BODY:
very light | light | medium | medium-full | full-bodied | heavy

ACIDITY:
tart | crisp | fresh | smooth | flabby

TANNINS (IF PRESENT):
LEVEL: low | medium | high   TYPE: soft | round | dry | hard

BALANCE:
good | fair | unbalanced (excess: alcohol - acid - tannin - sugar)

FLAVOR INTENSITY:
low | moderate | flavorful | powerful

FLAVORS:

FINISH:
short (< 3 sec) | medium (4-5) | long (5-7) | v. long (>8 sec)

CONCLUSION:

STYLE:
traditional | in-between | modern

rating: ☆ ☆ ☆ ☆ ☆

FOOD: **FOOD PAIRING:**
                 MATCH: perfect | good | neutral | bad

tasting date: location:

tasting partner(s):

wine name:

producer:

region/appellation:

grape varieties:

vintage: alcohol: price:

COLOR DEPTH:
watery | pale | medium | deep | dark

COLOR HUE:
WHITE: greenish | yellow | straw yellow | gold | amber
RED: purplish | ruby | red | garnet | brick | brown
ROSÉ: pink | salmon | orange | copper

CLARITY:
clear | slight haze | cloudy

AROMA INTENSITY:
low | moderate | aromatic | powerful

DEVELOPMENT:
youthful | some age | aged

AROMAS:

DRY/SWEET:
bone dry | dry | off dry | medium sweet | sweet | very sweet

BODY:
very light | light | medium | medium-full | full-bodied | heavy

ACIDITY:
tart | crisp | fresh | smooth | flabby

TANNINS (IF PRESENT):
LEVEL: low | medium | high   TYPE: soft | round | dry | hard

BALANCE:
good | fair | unbalanced (excess: alcohol - acid - tannin - sugar)

FLAVOR INTENSITY:
low | moderate | flavorful | powerful

FLAVORS:

FINISH:
short (< 3 sec) | medium (4-5) | long (5-7) | v. long (>8 sec)

CONCLUSION:

STYLE:
traditional | in-between | modern

rating: ☆ ☆ ☆ ☆ ☆

FOOD: **FOOD PAIRING:**

MATCH: perfect | good | neutral | bad

tasting date: location:

tasting partner(s):

wine name:

producer:

region/appellation:

grape varieties:

vintage: alcohol: price:

COLOR DEPTH:
watery | pale | medium | deep | dark

COLOR HUE:
WHITE: greenish | yellow | straw yellow | gold | amber
RED: purplish | ruby | red | garnet | brick | brown
ROSÉ: pink | salmon | orange | copper

CLARITY:
clear | slight haze | cloudy

AROMA INTENSITY:
low | moderate | aromatic | powerful

DEVELOPMENT:
youthful | some age | aged

AROMAS:

DRY/SWEET:
bone dry | dry | off dry | medium sweet | sweet | very sweet

BODY:
very light | light | medium | medium-full | full-bodied | heavy

ACIDITY:
tart | crisp | fresh | smooth | flabby

TANNINS (IF PRESENT):
LEVEL: low | medium | high   TYPE: soft | round | dry | hard

BALANCE:
good | fair | unbalanced (excess: alcohol - acid - tannin - sugar)

FLAVOR INTENSITY:
low | moderate | flavorful | powerful

FLAVORS:

FINISH:
short (< 3 sec) | medium (4-5) | long (5-7) | v. long (>8 sec)

CONCLUSION:

STYLE:
traditional | in-between | modern

rating: ☆ ☆ ☆ ☆ ☆

FOOD: **FOOD PAIRING:**
              MATCH: perfect | good | neutral | bad

tasting date: location:

tasting partner(s):

wine name:

producer:

region/appellation:

grape varieties:

vintage: alcohol: price:

COLOR DEPTH:
watery | pale | medium | deep | dark

COLOR HUE:
WHITE: greenish | yellow | straw yellow | gold | amber
RED: purplish | ruby | red | garnet | brick | brown
ROSÉ: pink | salmon | orange | copper

CLARITY:
clear | slight haze | cloudy

AROMA INTENSITY:
low | moderate | aromatic | powerful

DEVELOPMENT:
youthful | some age | aged

AROMAS:

DRY/SWEET:
bone dry | dry | off dry | medium sweet | sweet | very sweet

BODY:
very light | light | medium | medium-full | full-bodied | heavy

ACIDITY:
tart | crisp | fresh | smooth | flabby

TANNINS (IF PRESENT):
LEVEL: low | medium | high   TYPE: soft | round | dry | hard

BALANCE:
good | fair | unbalanced (excess: alcohol - acid - tannin - sugar)

FLAVOR INTENSITY:
low | moderate | flavorful | powerful

FLAVORS:

FINISH:
short (< 3 sec) | medium (4-5) | long (5-7) | v. long (>8 sec)

CONCLUSION:

STYLE:
traditional | in-between | modern

rating: ☆ ☆ ☆ ☆ ☆

FOOD: **FOOD PAIRING:**

MATCH: perfect | good | neutral | bad

tasting date: location:

tasting partner(s):

wine name:

producer:

region/appellation:

grape varieties:

vintage: alcohol: price:

COLOR DEPTH:
watery | pale | medium | deep | dark

COLOR HUE:
WHITE: greenish | yellow | straw yellow | gold | amber
RED: purplish | ruby | red | garnet | brick | brown
ROSÉ: pink | salmon | orange | copper

CLARITY:
clear | slight haze | cloudy

AROMA INTENSITY:
low | moderate | aromatic | powerful

DEVELOPMENT:
youthful | some age | aged

AROMAS:

DRY/SWEET:
bone dry | dry | off dry | medium sweet | sweet | very sweet

BODY:
very light | light | medium | medium-full | full-bodied | heavy

ACIDITY:
tart | crisp | fresh | smooth | flabby

TANNINS (IF PRESENT):
LEVEL: low | medium | high TYPE: soft | round | dry | hard

BALANCE:
good | fair | unbalanced (excess: alcohol - acid - tannin - sugar)

FLAVOR INTENSITY:
low | moderate | flavorful | powerful

FLAVORS:

FINISH:
short (< 3 sec) | medium (4-5) | long (5-7) | v. long (>8 sec)

CONCLUSION:

STYLE:
traditional | in-between | modern

rating: ☆ ☆ ☆ ☆ ☆

FOOD: **FOOD PAIRING:**
MATCH: perfect | good | neutral | bad

tasting date: location:

tasting partner(s):

wine name:

producer:

region/appellation:

grape varieties:

vintage: alcohol: price:

COLOR DEPTH:
watery | pale | medium | deep | dark

COLOR HUE:
WHITE: greenish | yellow | straw yellow | gold | amber
RED: purplish | ruby | red | garnet | brick | brown
ROSÉ: pink | salmon | orange | copper

CLARITY:
clear | slight haze | cloudy

AROMA INTENSITY:
low | moderate | aromatic | powerful

DEVELOPMENT:
youthful | some age | aged

AROMAS:

DRY/SWEET:
bone dry | dry | off dry | medium sweet | sweet | very sweet

BODY:
very light | light | medium | medium-full | full-bodied | heavy

ACIDITY:
tart | crisp | fresh | smooth | flabby

TANNINS (IF PRESENT):
LEVEL: low | medium | high   TYPE: soft | round | dry | hard

BALANCE:
good | fair | unbalanced (excess: alcohol - acid - tannin - sugar)

FLAVOR INTENSITY:
low | moderate | flavorful | powerful

FLAVORS:

FINISH:
short (< 3 sec) | medium (4-5) | long (5-7) | v. long (>8 sec)

CONCLUSION:

STYLE:
traditional | in-between | modern

rating: ☆ ☆ ☆ ☆ ☆

FOOD: **FOOD PAIRING:**
                   MATCH: perfect | good | neutral | bad

tasting date: location:

tasting partner(s):

wine name:

producer:

region/appellation:

grape varieties:

vintage: alcohol: price:

COLOR DEPTH:
watery | pale | medium | deep | dark

COLOR HUE:
WHITE: greenish | yellow | straw yellow | gold | amber
RED: purplish | ruby | red | garnet | brick | brown
ROSÉ: pink | salmon | orange | copper

CLARITY:
clear | slight haze | cloudy

AROMA INTENSITY:
low | moderate | aromatic | powerful

DEVELOPMENT:
youthful | some age | aged

AROMAS:

DRY/SWEET:
bone dry | dry | off dry | medium sweet | sweet | very sweet

BODY:
very light | light | medium | medium-full | full-bodied | heavy

ACIDITY:
tart | crisp | fresh | smooth | flabby

TANNINS (IF PRESENT):
LEVEL: low | medium | high   TYPE: soft | round | dry | hard

BALANCE:
good | fair | unbalanced (excess: alcohol - acid - tannin - sugar)

FLAVOR INTENSITY:
low | moderate | flavorful | powerful

FLAVORS:

FINISH:
short (< 3 sec) | medium (4-5) | long (5-7) | v. long (>8 sec)

CONCLUSION:

STYLE:
traditional | in-between | modern

rating: ☆ ☆ ☆ ☆ ☆

FOOD:

FOOD PAIRING:
MATCH: perfect | good | neutral | bad

tasting date: location:

tasting partner(s):

wine name:

producer:

region/appellation:

grape varieties:

vintage: alcohol: price:

COLOR DEPTH:
watery | pale | medium | deep | dark

COLOR HUE:
WHITE: greenish | yellow | straw yellow | gold | amber
RED: purplish | ruby | red | garnet | brick | brown
ROSÉ: pink | salmon | orange | copper

CLARITY:
clear | slight haze | cloudy

AROMA INTENSITY:
low | moderate | aromatic | powerful

DEVELOPMENT:
youthful | some age | aged

AROMAS:

DRY/SWEET:
bone dry | dry | off dry | medium sweet | sweet | very sweet

BODY:
very light | light | medium | medium-full | full-bodied | heavy

ACIDITY:
tart | crisp | fresh | smooth | flabby

TANNINS (IF PRESENT):
LEVEL: low | medium | high   TYPE: soft | round | dry | hard

BALANCE:
good | fair | unbalanced (excess: alcohol - acid - tannin - sugar)

FLAVOR INTENSITY:
low | moderate | flavorful | powerful

FLAVORS:

FINISH:
short (< 3 sec) | medium (4-5) | long (5-7) | v. long (>8 sec)

CONCLUSION:

STYLE:
traditional | in-between | modern

rating: ☆ ☆ ☆ ☆ ☆

FOOD: **FOOD PAIRING:**

MATCH: perfect | good | neutral | bad

tasting date: location:

tasting partner(s):

wine name:

producer:

region/appellation:

grape varieties:

vintage: alcohol: price:

COLOR DEPTH:
watery | pale | medium | deep | dark

COLOR HUE:
WHITE: greenish | yellow | straw yellow | gold | amber
RED: purplish | ruby | red | garnet | brick | brown
ROSÉ: pink | salmon | orange | copper

CLARITY:
clear | slight haze | cloudy

AROMA INTENSITY:
low | moderate | aromatic | powerful

DEVELOPMENT:
youthful | some age | aged

AROMAS:

DRY/SWEET:
bone dry | dry | off dry | medium sweet | sweet | very sweet

BODY:
very light | light | medium | medium-full | full-bodied | heavy

ACIDITY:
tart | crisp | fresh | smooth | flabby

TANNINS (IF PRESENT):
LEVEL: low | medium | high   TYPE: soft | round | dry | hard

BALANCE:
good | fair | unbalanced (excess: alcohol - acid - tannin - sugar)

FLAVOR INTENSITY:
low | moderate | flavorful | powerful

FLAVORS:

FINISH:
short (< 3 sec) | medium (4-5) | long (5-7) | v. long (>8 sec)

CONCLUSION:

STYLE:
traditional | in-between | modern

rating: ☆ ☆ ☆ ☆ ☆

FOOD: **FOOD PAIRING:**
MATCH: perfect | good | neutral | bad

tasting date: location:

tasting partner(s):

wine name:

producer:

region/appellation:

grape varieties:

vintage: alcohol: price:

COLOR DEPTH:
watery | pale | medium | deep | dark

COLOR HUE:
WHITE: greenish | yellow | straw yellow | gold | amber
RED: purplish | ruby | red | garnet | brick | brown
ROSÉ: pink | salmon | orange | copper

CLARITY:
clear | slight haze | cloudy

AROMA INTENSITY:
low | moderate | aromatic | powerful

DEVELOPMENT:
youthful | some age | aged

AROMAS:

DRY/SWEET:
bone dry | dry | off dry | medium sweet | sweet | very sweet

BODY:
very light | light | medium | medium-full | full-bodied | heavy

ACIDITY:
tart | crisp | fresh | smooth | flabby

TANNINS (IF PRESENT):
LEVEL: low | medium | high   TYPE: soft | round | dry | hard

BALANCE:
good | fair | unbalanced (excess: alcohol - acid - tannin - sugar)

FLAVOR INTENSITY:
low | moderate | flavorful | powerful

FLAVORS:

FINISH:
short (< 3 sec) | medium (4-5) | long (5-7) | v. long (>8 sec)

CONCLUSION:

STYLE:
traditional | in-between | modern

rating: ☆ ☆ ☆ ☆ ☆

FOOD: **FOOD PAIRING:**

MATCH: perfect | good | neutral | bad

tasting date: location:

tasting partner(s):

wine name:

producer:

region/appellation:

grape varieties:

vintage: alcohol: price:

COLOR DEPTH:
watery | pale | medium | deep | dark

COLOR HUE:
WHITE: greenish | yellow | straw yellow | gold | amber
RED: purplish | ruby | red | garnet | brick | brown
ROSÉ: pink | salmon | orange | copper

CLARITY:
clear | slight haze | cloudy

AROMA INTENSITY:
low | moderate | aromatic | powerful

DEVELOPMENT:
youthful | some age | aged

AROMAS:

DRY/SWEET:
bone dry | dry | off dry | medium sweet | sweet | very sweet

BODY:
very light | light | medium | medium-full | full-bodied | heavy

ACIDITY:
tart | crisp | fresh | smooth | flabby

TANNINS (IF PRESENT):
LEVEL: low | medium | high   TYPE: soft | round | dry | hard

BALANCE:
good | fair | unbalanced (excess: alcohol - acid - tannin - sugar)

FLAVOR INTENSITY:
low | moderate | flavorful | powerful

FLAVORS:

FINISH:
short (< 3 sec) | medium (4-5) | long (5-7) | v. long (>8 sec)

CONCLUSION:

STYLE:
traditional | in-between | modern

rating: ☆ ☆ ☆ ☆ ☆

FOOD: **FOOD PAIRING:**
              MATCH: perfect | good | neutral | bad

tasting date: location:

tasting partner(s):

wine name:

producer:

region/appellation:

grape varieties:

vintage: alcohol: price:

COLOR DEPTH:
watery | pale | medium | deep | dark

COLOR HUE:
WHITE: greenish | yellow | straw yellow | gold | amber
RED: purplish | ruby | red | garnet | brick | brown
ROSÉ: pink | salmon | orange | copper

CLARITY:
clear | slight haze | cloudy

AROMA INTENSITY:
low | moderate | aromatic | powerful

DEVELOPMENT:
youthful | some age | aged

AROMAS:

DRY/SWEET:
bone dry | dry | off dry | medium sweet | sweet | very sweet

BODY:
very light | light | medium | medium-full | full-bodied | heavy

ACIDITY:
tart | crisp | fresh | smooth | flabby

TANNINS (IF PRESENT):
LEVEL: low | medium | high   TYPE: soft | round | dry | hard

BALANCE:
good | fair | unbalanced (excess: alcohol - acid - tannin - sugar)

FLAVOR INTENSITY:
low | moderate | flavorful | powerful

FLAVORS:

FINISH:
short (< 3 sec) | medium (4-5) | long (5-7) | v. long (>8 sec)

CONCLUSION:

STYLE:
traditional | in-between | modern

rating: ☆ ☆ ☆ ☆ ☆

FOOD: ## FOOD PAIRING:
              MATCH: perfect | good | neutral | bad

tasting date: location:

tasting partner(s):

wine name:

producer:

region/appellation:

grape varieties:

vintage: alcohol: price:

COLOR DEPTH:
watery | pale | medium | deep | dark

COLOR HUE:
WHITE: greenish | yellow | straw yellow | gold | amber
RED: purplish | ruby | red | garnet | brick | brown
ROSÉ: pink | salmon | orange | copper

CLARITY:
clear | slight haze | cloudy

AROMA INTENSITY:
low | moderate | aromatic | powerful

DEVELOPMENT:
youthful | some age | aged

AROMAS:

DRY/SWEET:
bone dry | dry | off dry | medium sweet | sweet | very sweet

BODY:
very light | light | medium | medium-full | full-bodied | heavy

ACIDITY:
tart | crisp | fresh | smooth | flabby

TANNINS (IF PRESENT):
LEVEL: low | medium | high   TYPE: soft | round | dry | hard

BALANCE:
good | fair | unbalanced (excess: alcohol - acid - tannin - sugar)

FLAVOR INTENSITY:
low | moderate | flavorful | powerful

FLAVORS:

FINISH:
short (< 3 sec) | medium (4-5) | long (5-7) | v. long (>8 sec)

CONCLUSION:

STYLE:
traditional | in-between | modern

rating: ☆ ☆ ☆ ☆ ☆

FOOD: **FOOD PAIRING:**
MATCH: perfect | good | neutral | bad

tasting date: location:

tasting partner(s):

wine name:

producer:

region/appellation:

grape varieties:

vintage: alcohol: price:

COLOR DEPTH:
watery | pale | medium | deep | dark

COLOR HUE:
WHITE: greenish | yellow | straw yellow | gold | amber
RED: purplish | ruby | red | garnet | brick | brown
ROSÉ: pink | salmon | orange | copper

CLARITY:
clear | slight haze | cloudy

AROMA INTENSITY:
low | moderate | aromatic | powerful

DEVELOPMENT:
youthful | some age | aged

AROMAS:

DRY/SWEET:
bone dry | dry | off dry | medium sweet | sweet | very sweet

BODY:
very light | light | medium | medium-full | full-bodied | heavy

ACIDITY:
tart | crisp | fresh | smooth | flabby

TANNINS (IF PRESENT):
LEVEL: low | medium | high   TYPE: soft | round | dry | hard

BALANCE:
good | fair | unbalanced (excess: alcohol - acid - tannin - sugar)

FLAVOR INTENSITY:
low | moderate | flavorful | powerful

FLAVORS:

FINISH:
short (< 3 sec) | medium (4-5) | long (5-7) | v. long (>8 sec)

CONCLUSION:

STYLE:
traditional | in-between | modern

rating: ☆ ☆ ☆ ☆ ☆

FOOD: **FOOD PAIRING:**

MATCH: perfect | good | neutral | bad

tasting date: location:

tasting partner(s):

wine name:

producer:

region/appellation:

grape varieties:

vintage: alcohol: price:

COLOR DEPTH:
watery | pale | medium | deep | dark

COLOR HUE:
WHITE: greenish | yellow | straw yellow | gold | amber
RED: purplish | ruby | red | garnet | brick | brown
ROSÉ: pink | salmon | orange | copper

CLARITY:
clear | slight haze | cloudy

AROMA INTENSITY:
low | moderate | aromatic | powerful

DEVELOPMENT:
youthful | some age | aged

AROMAS:

DRY/SWEET:
bone dry | dry | off dry | medium sweet | sweet | very sweet

BODY:
very light | light | medium | medium-full | full-bodied | heavy

ACIDITY:
tart | crisp | fresh | smooth | flabby

TANNINS (IF PRESENT):
LEVEL: low | medium | high   TYPE: soft | round | dry | hard

BALANCE:
good | fair | unbalanced (excess: alcohol - acid - tannin - sugar)

FLAVOR INTENSITY:
low | moderate | flavorful | powerful

FLAVORS:

FINISH:
short (< 3 sec) | medium (4-5) | long (5-7) | v. long (>8 sec)

CONCLUSION:

STYLE:
traditional | in-between | modern

rating: ☆ ☆ ☆ ☆ ☆

FOOD: **FOOD PAIRING:**
                          MATCH: perfect | good | neutral | bad

tasting date: location:

tasting partner(s):

wine name:

producer:

region/appellation:

grape varieties:

vintage: alcohol: price:

COLOR DEPTH:
watery | pale | medium | deep | dark

COLOR HUE:
WHITE: greenish | yellow | straw yellow | gold | amber
RED: purplish | ruby | red | garnet | brick | brown
ROSÉ: pink | salmon | orange | copper

CLARITY:
clear | slight haze | cloudy

AROMA INTENSITY:
low | moderate | aromatic | powerful

DEVELOPMENT:
youthful | some age | aged

AROMAS:

DRY/SWEET:
bone dry | dry | off dry | medium sweet | sweet | very sweet

BODY:
very light | light | medium | medium-full | full-bodied | heavy

ACIDITY:
tart | crisp | fresh | smooth | flabby

TANNINS (IF PRESENT):
LEVEL: low | medium | high   TYPE: soft | round | dry | hard

BALANCE:
good | fair | unbalanced (excess: alcohol - acid - tannin - sugar)

FLAVOR INTENSITY:
low | moderate | flavorful | powerful

FLAVORS:

FINISH:
short (< 3 sec) | medium (4-5) | long (5-7) | v. long (>8 sec)

CONCLUSION:

STYLE:
traditional | in-between | modern

rating: ☆ ☆ ☆ ☆ ☆

FOOD: **FOOD PAIRING:**

MATCH: perfect | good | neutral | bad

tasting date: location:

tasting partner(s):

wine name:

producer:

region/appellation:

grape varieties:

vintage: alcohol: price:

COLOR DEPTH:
watery | pale | medium | deep | dark

COLOR HUE:
WHITE: greenish | yellow | straw yellow | gold | amber
RED: purplish | ruby | red | garnet | brick | brown
ROSÉ: pink | salmon | orange | copper

CLARITY:
clear | slight haze | cloudy

AROMA INTENSITY:
low | moderate | aromatic | powerful

DEVELOPMENT:
youthful | some age | aged

AROMAS:

DRY/SWEET:
bone dry | dry | off dry | medium sweet | sweet | very sweet

BODY:
very light | light | medium | medium-full | full-bodied | heavy

ACIDITY:
tart | crisp | fresh | smooth | flabby

TANNINS (IF PRESENT):
LEVEL: low | medium | high   TYPE: soft | round | dry | hard

BALANCE:
good | fair | unbalanced (excess: alcohol - acid - tannin - sugar)

FLAVOR INTENSITY:
low | moderate | flavorful | powerful

FLAVORS:

FINISH:
short (< 3 sec) | medium (4-5) | long (5-7) | v. long (>8 sec)

CONCLUSION:

STYLE:
traditional | in-between | modern

rating: ☆ ☆ ☆ ☆ ☆

FOOD: **FOOD PAIRING:**
MATCH: perfect | good | neutral | bad

tasting date: location:

tasting partner(s):

wine name:

producer:

region/appellation:

grape varieties:

vintage: alcohol: price:

COLOR DEPTH:
watery | pale | medium | deep | dark

COLOR HUE:
WHITE: greenish | yellow | straw yellow | gold | amber
RED: purplish | ruby | red | garnet | brick | brown
ROSÉ: pink | salmon | orange | copper

CLARITY:
clear | slight haze | cloudy

AROMA INTENSITY:
low | moderate | aromatic | powerful

DEVELOPMENT:
youthful | some age | aged

AROMAS:

DRY/SWEET:
bone dry | dry | off dry | medium sweet | sweet | very sweet

BODY:
very light | light | medium | medium-full | full-bodied | heavy

ACIDITY:
tart | crisp | fresh | smooth | flabby

TANNINS (IF PRESENT):
LEVEL: low | medium | high   TYPE: soft | round | dry | hard

BALANCE:
good | fair | unbalanced (excess: alcohol - acid - tannin - sugar)

FLAVOR INTENSITY:
low | moderate | flavorful | powerful

FLAVORS:

FINISH:
short (< 3 sec) | medium (4-5) | long (5-7) | v. long (>8 sec)

CONCLUSION:

STYLE:
traditional | in-between | modern

rating: ☆ ☆ ☆ ☆ ☆

FOOD: **FOOD PAIRING:**

MATCH: perfect | good | neutral | bad

tasting date: location:

tasting partner(s):

wine name:

producer:

region/appellation:

grape varieties:

vintage: alcohol: price:

COLOR DEPTH:
watery | pale | medium | deep | dark

COLOR HUE:
WHITE: greenish | yellow | straw yellow | gold | amber
RED: purplish | ruby | red | garnet | brick | brown
ROSÉ: pink | salmon | orange | copper

CLARITY:
clear | slight haze | cloudy

AROMA INTENSITY:
low | moderate | aromatic | powerful

DEVELOPMENT:
youthful | some age | aged

AROMAS:

DRY/SWEET:
bone dry | dry | off dry | medium sweet | sweet | very sweet

BODY:
very light | light | medium | medium-full | full-bodied | heavy

ACIDITY:
tart | crisp | fresh | smooth | flabby

TANNINS (IF PRESENT):
LEVEL: low | medium | high   TYPE: soft | round | dry | hard

BALANCE:
good | fair | unbalanced (excess: alcohol - acid - tannin - sugar)

FLAVOR INTENSITY:
low | moderate | flavorful | powerful

FLAVORS:

FINISH:
short (< 3 sec) | medium (4-5) | long (5-7) | v. long (>8 sec)

CONCLUSION:

STYLE:
traditional | in-between | modern

rating: ☆ ☆ ☆ ☆ ☆

FOOD: ## FOOD PAIRING:
MATCH: perfect | good | neutral | bad

tasting date: location:

tasting partner(s):

wine name:

producer:

region/appellation:

grape varieties:

vintage: alcohol: price:

COLOR DEPTH:
watery | pale | medium | deep | dark

COLOR HUE:
WHITE: greenish | yellow | straw yellow | gold | amber
RED: purplish | ruby | red | garnet | brick | brown
ROSÉ: pink | salmon | orange | copper

CLARITY:
clear | slight haze | cloudy

AROMA INTENSITY:
low | moderate | aromatic | powerful

DEVELOPMENT:
youthful | some age | aged

AROMAS:

DRY/SWEET:
bone dry | dry | off dry | medium sweet | sweet | very sweet

BODY:
very light | light | medium | medium-full | full-bodied | heavy

ACIDITY:
tart | crisp | fresh | smooth | flabby

TANNINS (IF PRESENT):
LEVEL: low | medium | high   TYPE: soft | round | dry | hard

BALANCE:
good | fair | unbalanced (excess: alcohol - acid - tannin - sugar)

FLAVOR INTENSITY:
low | moderate | flavorful | powerful

FLAVORS:

FINISH:
short (< 3 sec) | medium (4-5) | long (5-7) | v. long (>8 sec)

CONCLUSION:

STYLE:
traditional | in-between | modern

rating: ☆ ☆ ☆ ☆ ☆

FOOD: **FOOD PAIRING:**

MATCH: perfect | good | neutral | bad

tasting date: location:

tasting partner(s):

wine name:

producer:

region/appellation:

grape varieties:

vintage: alcohol: price:

COLOR DEPTH:
watery | pale | medium | deep | dark
COLOR HUE:
WHITE: greenish | yellow | straw yellow | gold | amber
RED: purplish | ruby | red | garnet | brick | brown
ROSÉ: pink | salmon | orange | copper

CLARITY:
clear | slight haze | cloudy

AROMA INTENSITY:
low | moderate | aromatic | powerful
DEVELOPMENT:
youthful | some age | aged
AROMAS:

DRY/SWEET:
bone dry | dry | off dry | medium sweet | sweet | very sweet
BODY:
very light | light | medium | medium-full | full-bodied | heavy
ACIDITY:
tart | crisp | fresh | smooth | flabby
TANNINS (IF PRESENT):
LEVEL: low | medium | high   TYPE: soft | round | dry | hard
BALANCE:
good | fair | unbalanced (excess: alcohol - acid - tannin - sugar)
FLAVOR INTENSITY:
low | moderate | flavorful | powerful
FLAVORS:

FINISH:
short (< 3 sec) | medium (4-5) | long (5-7) | v. long (>8 sec)
CONCLUSION:

STYLE:
traditional | in-between | modern

rating: ☆ ☆ ☆ ☆ ☆

FOOD: **FOOD PAIRING:**
                MATCH: perfect | good | neutral | bad

tasting date: location:

tasting partner(s):

wine name:

producer:

region/appellation:

grape varieties:

vintage: alcohol: price:

COLOR DEPTH:
watery | pale | medium | deep | dark

COLOR HUE:
WHITE: greenish | yellow | straw yellow | gold | amber
RED: purplish | ruby | red | garnet | brick | brown
ROSÉ: pink | salmon | orange | copper

CLARITY:
clear | slight haze | cloudy

AROMA INTENSITY:
low | moderate | aromatic | powerful

DEVELOPMENT:
youthful | some age | aged

AROMAS:

DRY/SWEET:
bone dry | dry | off dry | medium sweet | sweet | very sweet

BODY:
very light | light | medium | medium-full | full-bodied | heavy

ACIDITY:
tart | crisp | fresh | smooth | flabby

TANNINS (IF PRESENT):
LEVEL: low | medium | high   TYPE: soft | round | dry | hard

BALANCE:
good | fair | unbalanced (excess: alcohol - acid - tannin - sugar)

FLAVOR INTENSITY:
low | moderate | flavorful | powerful

FLAVORS:

FINISH:
short (< 3 sec) | medium (4-5) | long (5-7) | v. long (>8 sec)

CONCLUSION:

STYLE:
traditional | in-between | modern

rating: ☆ ☆ ☆ ☆ ☆

FOOD: **FOOD PAIRING:**

MATCH: perfect | good | neutral | bad

tasting date: location:

tasting partner(s):

wine name:

producer:

region/appellation:

grape varieties:

vintage: alcohol: price:

COLOR DEPTH:
watery | pale | medium | deep | dark

COLOR HUE:
WHITE: greenish | yellow | straw yellow | gold | amber
RED: purplish | ruby | red | garnet | brick | brown
ROSÉ: pink | salmon | orange | copper

CLARITY:
clear | slight haze | cloudy

AROMA INTENSITY:
low | moderate | aromatic | powerful

DEVELOPMENT:
youthful | some age | aged

AROMAS:

DRY/SWEET:
bone dry | dry | off dry | medium sweet | sweet | very sweet

BODY:
very light | light | medium | medium-full | full-bodied | heavy

ACIDITY:
tart | crisp | fresh | smooth | flabby

TANNINS (IF PRESENT):
LEVEL: low | medium | high   TYPE: soft | round | dry | hard

BALANCE:
good | fair | unbalanced (excess: alcohol - acid - tannin - sugar)

FLAVOR INTENSITY:
low | moderate | flavorful | powerful

FLAVORS:

FINISH:
short (< 3 sec) | medium (4-5) | long (5-7) | v. long (>8 sec)

CONCLUSION:

STYLE:
traditional | in-between | modern

rating: ☆ ☆ ☆ ☆ ☆

FOOD: ### FOOD PAIRING:
MATCH: perfect | good | neutral | bad

tasting date: location:

tasting partner(s):

wine name:

producer:

region/appellation:

grape varieties:

vintage: alcohol: price:

COLOR DEPTH:
watery | pale | medium | deep | dark

COLOR HUE:
WHITE: greenish | yellow | straw yellow | gold | amber
RED: purplish | ruby | red | garnet | brick | brown
ROSÉ: pink | salmon | orange | copper

CLARITY:
clear | slight haze | cloudy

AROMA INTENSITY:
low | moderate | aromatic | powerful

DEVELOPMENT:
youthful | some age | aged

AROMAS:

DRY/SWEET:
bone dry | dry | off dry | medium sweet | sweet | very sweet

BODY:
very light | light | medium | medium-full | full-bodied | heavy

ACIDITY:
tart | crisp | fresh | smooth | flabby

TANNINS (IF PRESENT):
LEVEL: low | medium | high   TYPE: soft | round | dry | hard

BALANCE:
good | fair | unbalanced (excess: alcohol - acid - tannin - sugar)

FLAVOR INTENSITY:
low | moderate | flavorful | powerful

FLAVORS:

FINISH:
short (< 3 sec) | medium (4-5) | long (5-7) | v. long (>8 sec)

CONCLUSION:

STYLE:
traditional | in-between | modern

rating: ☆ ☆ ☆ ☆ ☆

FOOD: **FOOD PAIRING:**
                         MATCH: perfect | good | neutral | bad

tasting date: location:

tasting partner(s):

wine name:

producer:

region/appellation:

grape varieties:

vintage: alcohol: price:

COLOR DEPTH:
watery | pale | medium | deep | dark
COLOR HUE:
WHITE: greenish | yellow | straw yellow | gold | amber
RED: purplish | ruby | red | garnet | brick | brown
ROSÉ: pink | salmon | orange | copper
CLARITY:
clear | slight haze | cloudy

AROMA INTENSITY:
low | moderate | aromatic | powerful
DEVELOPMENT:
youthful | some age | aged
AROMAS:

DRY/SWEET:
bone dry | dry | off dry | medium sweet | sweet | very sweet
BODY:
very light | light | medium | medium-full | full-bodied | heavy
ACIDITY:
tart | crisp | fresh | smooth | flabby
TANNINS (IF PRESENT):
LEVEL: low | medium | high   TYPE: soft | round | dry | hard
BALANCE:
good | fair | unbalanced (excess: alcohol - acid - tannin - sugar)
FLAVOR INTENSITY:
low | moderate | flavorful | powerful
FLAVORS:

FINISH:
short (< 3 sec) | medium (4-5) | long (5-7) | v. long (>8 sec)
CONCLUSION:

STYLE:
traditional | in-between | modern

rating: ☆ ☆ ☆ ☆ ☆

FOOD: **FOOD PAIRING:**

MATCH: perfect | good | neutral | bad

tasting date: location:

tasting partner(s):

wine name:

producer:

region/appellation:

grape varieties:

vintage: alcohol: price:

COLOR DEPTH:
watery | pale | medium | deep | dark

COLOR HUE:
WHITE: greenish | yellow | straw yellow | gold | amber
RED: purplish | ruby | red | garnet | brick | brown
ROSÉ: pink | salmon | orange | copper

CLARITY:
clear | slight haze | cloudy

AROMA INTENSITY:
low | moderate | aromatic | powerful

DEVELOPMENT:
youthful | some age | aged

AROMAS:

DRY/SWEET:
bone dry | dry | off dry | medium sweet | sweet | very sweet

BODY:
very light | light | medium | medium-full | full-bodied | heavy

ACIDITY:
tart | crisp | fresh | smooth | flabby

TANNINS (IF PRESENT):
LEVEL: low | medium | high   TYPE: soft | round | dry | hard

BALANCE:
good | fair | unbalanced (excess: alcohol - acid - tannin - sugar)

FLAVOR INTENSITY:
low | moderate | flavorful | powerful

FLAVORS:

FINISH:
short (< 3 sec) | medium (4-5) | long (5-7) | v. long (>8 sec)

CONCLUSION:

STYLE:
traditional | in-between | modern

rating: ☆ ☆ ☆ ☆ ☆

FOOD: **FOOD PAIRING:**
                  MATCH: perfect | good | neutral | bad

tasting date: location:

tasting partner(s):

wine name:

producer:

region/appellation:

grape varieties:

vintage: alcohol: price:

COLOR DEPTH:
watery | pale | medium | deep | dark

COLOR HUE:
WHITE: greenish | yellow | straw yellow | gold | amber
RED: purplish | ruby | red | garnet | brick | brown
ROSÉ: pink | salmon | orange | copper

CLARITY:
clear | slight haze | cloudy

AROMA INTENSITY:
low | moderate | aromatic | powerful

DEVELOPMENT:
youthful | some age | aged

AROMAS:

DRY/SWEET:
bone dry | dry | off dry | medium sweet | sweet | very sweet

BODY:
very light | light | medium | medium-full | full-bodied | heavy

ACIDITY:
tart | crisp | fresh | smooth | flabby

TANNINS (IF PRESENT):
LEVEL: low | medium | high   TYPE: soft | round | dry | hard

BALANCE:
good | fair | unbalanced (excess: alcohol - acid - tannin - sugar)

FLAVOR INTENSITY:
low | moderate | flavorful | powerful

FLAVORS:

FINISH:
short (< 3 sec) | medium (4-5) | long (5-7) | v. long (>8 sec)

CONCLUSION:

STYLE:
traditional | in-between | modern

rating: ☆ ☆ ☆ ☆ ☆

FOOD: **FOOD PAIRING:**
MATCH: perfect | good | neutral | bad

tasting date: location:

tasting partner(s):

wine name:

producer:

region/appellation:

grape varieties:

vintage: alcohol: price:

COLOR DEPTH:
watery | pale | medium | deep | dark

COLOR HUE:
WHITE: greenish | yellow | straw yellow | gold | amber
RED: purplish | ruby | red | garnet | brick | brown
ROSÉ: pink | salmon | orange | copper

CLARITY:
clear | slight haze | cloudy

AROMA INTENSITY:
low | moderate | aromatic | powerful

DEVELOPMENT:
youthful | some age | aged

AROMAS:

DRY/SWEET:
bone dry | dry | off dry | medium sweet | sweet | very sweet

BODY:
very light | light | medium | medium-full | full-bodied | heavy

ACIDITY:
tart | crisp | fresh | smooth | flabby

TANNINS (IF PRESENT):
LEVEL: low | medium | high   TYPE: soft | round | dry | hard

BALANCE:
good | fair | unbalanced (excess: alcohol - acid - tannin - sugar)

FLAVOR INTENSITY:
low | moderate | flavorful | powerful

FLAVORS:

FINISH:
short (< 3 sec) | medium (4-5) | long (5-7) | v. long (>8 sec)

CONCLUSION:

STYLE:
traditional | in-between | modern

rating: ☆ ☆ ☆ ☆ ☆

FOOD: **FOOD PAIRING:**

MATCH: perfect | good | neutral | bad

tasting date: location:

tasting partner(s):

wine name:

producer:

region/appellation:

grape varieties:

vintage: alcohol: price:

COLOR DEPTH:
watery | pale | medium | deep | dark

COLOR HUE:
WHITE: greenish | yellow | straw yellow | gold | amber
RED: purplish | ruby | red | garnet | brick | brown
ROSÉ: pink | salmon | orange | copper

CLARITY:
clear | slight haze | cloudy

AROMA INTENSITY:
low | moderate | aromatic | powerful

DEVELOPMENT:
youthful | some age | aged

AROMAS:

DRY/SWEET:
bone dry | dry | off dry | medium sweet | sweet | very sweet

BODY:
very light | light | medium | medium-full | full-bodied | heavy

ACIDITY:
tart | crisp | fresh | smooth | flabby

TANNINS (IF PRESENT):
LEVEL: low | medium | high   TYPE: soft | round | dry | hard

BALANCE:
good | fair | unbalanced (excess: alcohol - acid - tannin - sugar)

FLAVOR INTENSITY:
low | moderate | flavorful | powerful

FLAVORS:

FINISH:
short (< 3 sec) | medium (4-5) | long (5-7) | v. long (>8 sec)

CONCLUSION:

STYLE:
traditional | in-between | modern

rating: ☆ ☆ ☆ ☆ ☆

FOOD: **FOOD PAIRING:**
             MATCH: perfect | good | neutral | bad

tasting date: location:

tasting partner(s):

wine name:

producer:

region/appellation:

grape varieties:

vintage: alcohol: price:

COLOR DEPTH:
watery | pale | medium | deep | dark

COLOR HUE:
WHITE: greenish | yellow | straw yellow | gold | amber
RED: purplish | ruby | red | garnet | brick | brown
ROSÉ: pink | salmon | orange | copper

CLARITY:
clear | slight haze | cloudy

AROMA INTENSITY:
low | moderate | aromatic | powerful

DEVELOPMENT:
youthful | some age | aged

AROMAS:

DRY/SWEET:
bone dry | dry | off dry | medium sweet | sweet | very sweet

BODY:
very light | light | medium | medium-full | full-bodied | heavy

ACIDITY:
tart | crisp | fresh | smooth | flabby

TANNINS (IF PRESENT):
LEVEL: low | medium | high   TYPE: soft | round | dry | hard

BALANCE:
good | fair | unbalanced (excess: alcohol - acid - tannin - sugar)

FLAVOR INTENSITY:
low | moderate | flavorful | powerful

FLAVORS:

FINISH:
short (< 3 sec) | medium (4-5) | long (5-7) | v. long (>8 sec)

CONCLUSION:

STYLE:
traditional | in-between | modern

rating: ☆ ☆ ☆ ☆ ☆

FOOD: **FOOD PAIRING:**
                    MATCH: perfect | good | neutral | bad

tasting date: location:

tasting partner(s):

wine name:

producer:

region/appellation:

grape varieties:

vintage: alcohol: price:

COLOR DEPTH:
watery | pale | medium | deep | dark
COLOR HUE:
WHITE: greenish | yellow | straw yellow | gold | amber
RED: purplish | ruby | red | garnet | brick | brown
ROSÉ: pink | salmon | orange | copper
CLARITY:
clear | slight haze | cloudy

AROMA INTENSITY:
low | moderate | aromatic | powerful
DEVELOPMENT:
youthful | some age | aged
AROMAS:

DRY/SWEET:
bone dry | dry | off dry | medium sweet | sweet | very sweet
BODY:
very light | light | medium | medium-full | full-bodied | heavy
ACIDITY:
tart | crisp | fresh | smooth | flabby
TANNINS (IF PRESENT):
LEVEL: low | medium | high   TYPE: soft | round | dry | hard
BALANCE:
good | fair | unbalanced (excess: alcohol - acid - tannin - sugar)
FLAVOR INTENSITY:
low | moderate | flavorful | powerful
FLAVORS:

FINISH:
short (< 3 sec) | medium (4-5) | long (5-7) | v. long (>8 sec)
CONCLUSION:

STYLE:
traditional | in-between | modern

rating: ☆ ☆ ☆ ☆ ☆

FOOD: **FOOD PAIRING:**
                        MATCH: perfect | good | neutral | bad

tasting date: location:

tasting partner(s):

wine name:

producer:

region/appellation:

grape varieties:

vintage: alcohol: price:

COLOR DEPTH:
watery | pale | medium | deep | dark

COLOR HUE:
WHITE: greenish | yellow | straw yellow | gold | amber
RED: purplish | ruby | red | garnet | brick | brown
ROSÉ: pink | salmon | orange | copper

CLARITY:
clear | slight haze | cloudy

AROMA INTENSITY:
low | moderate | aromatic | powerful

DEVELOPMENT:
youthful | some age | aged

AROMAS:

DRY/SWEET:
bone dry | dry | off dry | medium sweet | sweet | very sweet

BODY:
very light | light | medium | medium-full | full-bodied | heavy

ACIDITY:
tart | crisp | fresh | smooth | flabby

TANNINS (IF PRESENT):
LEVEL: low | medium | high   TYPE: soft | round | dry | hard

BALANCE:
good | fair | unbalanced (excess: alcohol - acid - tannin - sugar)

FLAVOR INTENSITY:
low | moderate | flavorful | powerful

FLAVORS:

FINISH:
short (< 3 sec) | medium (4-5) | long (5-7) | v. long (>8 sec)

CONCLUSION:

STYLE:
traditional | in-between | modern

rating: ☆ ☆ ☆ ☆ ☆

FOOD: **FOOD PAIRING:**

MATCH: perfect | good | neutral | bad

tasting date: location:

tasting partner(s):

wine name:

producer:

region/appellation:

grape varieties:

vintage: alcohol: price:

COLOR DEPTH:
watery | pale | medium | deep | dark

COLOR HUE:
WHITE: greenish | yellow | straw yellow | gold | amber
RED: purplish | ruby | red | garnet | brick | brown
ROSÉ: pink | salmon | orange | copper

CLARITY:
clear | slight haze | cloudy

AROMA INTENSITY:
low | moderate | aromatic | powerful

DEVELOPMENT:
youthful | some age | aged

AROMAS:

DRY/SWEET:
bone dry | dry | off dry | medium sweet | sweet | very sweet

BODY:
very light | light | medium | medium-full | full-bodied | heavy

ACIDITY:
tart | crisp | fresh | smooth | flabby

TANNINS (IF PRESENT):
LEVEL: low | medium | high   TYPE: soft | round | dry | hard

BALANCE:
good | fair | unbalanced (excess: alcohol - acid - tannin - sugar)

FLAVOR INTENSITY:
low | moderate | flavorful | powerful

FLAVORS:

FINISH:
short (< 3 sec) | medium (4-5) | long (5-7) | v. long (>8 sec)

CONCLUSION:

STYLE:
traditional | in-between | modern

rating: ☆ ☆ ☆ ☆ ☆

FOOD: **FOOD PAIRING:**

MATCH: perfect | good | neutral | bad

tasting date: location:

tasting partner(s):

wine name:

producer:

region/appellation:

grape varieties:

vintage: alcohol: price:

COLOR DEPTH:
watery | pale | medium | deep | dark

COLOR HUE:
WHITE: greenish | yellow | straw yellow | gold | amber
RED: purplish | ruby | red | garnet | brick | brown
ROSÉ: pink | salmon | orange | copper

CLARITY:
clear | slight haze | cloudy

AROMA INTENSITY:
low | moderate | aromatic | powerful

DEVELOPMENT:
youthful | some age | aged

AROMAS:

DRY/SWEET:
bone dry | dry | off dry | medium sweet | sweet | very sweet

BODY:
very light | light | medium | medium-full | full-bodied | heavy

ACIDITY:
tart | crisp | fresh | smooth | flabby

TANNINS (IF PRESENT):
LEVEL: low | medium | high   TYPE: soft | round | dry | hard

BALANCE:
good | fair | unbalanced (excess: alcohol - acid - tannin - sugar)

FLAVOR INTENSITY:
low | moderate | flavorful | powerful

FLAVORS:

FINISH:
short (< 3 sec) | medium (4-5) | long (5-7) | v. long (>8 sec)

CONCLUSION:

STYLE:
traditional | in-between | modern

rating: ☆ ☆ ☆ ☆ ☆

FOOD: **FOOD PAIRING:**

MATCH: perfect | good | neutral | bad

tasting date: location:

tasting partner(s):

wine name:

producer:

region/appellation:

grape varieties:

vintage: alcohol: price:

COLOR DEPTH:
watery | pale | medium | deep | dark

COLOR HUE:
WHITE: greenish | yellow | straw yellow | gold | amber
RED: purplish | ruby | red | garnet | brick | brown
ROSÉ: pink | salmon | orange | copper

CLARITY:
clear | slight haze | cloudy

AROMA INTENSITY:
low | moderate | aromatic | powerful

DEVELOPMENT:
youthful | some age | aged

AROMAS:

DRY/SWEET:
bone dry | dry | off dry | medium sweet | sweet | very sweet

BODY:
very light | light | medium | medium-full | full-bodied | heavy

ACIDITY:
tart | crisp | fresh | smooth | flabby

TANNINS (IF PRESENT):
LEVEL: low | medium | high   TYPE: soft | round | dry | hard

BALANCE:
good | fair | unbalanced (excess: alcohol - acid - tannin - sugar)

FLAVOR INTENSITY:
low | moderate | flavorful | powerful

FLAVORS:

FINISH:
short (< 3 sec) | medium (4-5) | long (5-7) | v. long (>8 sec)

CONCLUSION:

STYLE:
traditional | in-between | modern

rating: ☆ ☆ ☆ ☆ ☆

FOOD: FOOD PAIRING:
MATCH: perfect | good | neutral | bad

tasting date: location:

tasting partner(s):

wine name:

producer:

region/appellation:

grape varieties:

vintage: alcohol: price:

COLOR DEPTH:
watery | pale | medium | deep | dark

COLOR HUE:
WHITE: greenish | yellow | straw yellow | gold | amber
RED: purplish | ruby | red | garnet | brick | brown
ROSÉ: pink | salmon | orange | copper

CLARITY:
clear | slight haze | cloudy

AROMA INTENSITY:
low | moderate | aromatic | powerful

DEVELOPMENT:
youthful | some age | aged

AROMAS:

DRY/SWEET:
bone dry | dry | off dry | medium sweet | sweet | very sweet

BODY:
very light | light | medium | medium-full | full-bodied | heavy

ACIDITY:
tart | crisp | fresh | smooth | flabby

TANNINS (IF PRESENT):
LEVEL: low | medium | high   TYPE: soft | round | dry | hard

BALANCE:
good | fair | unbalanced (excess: alcohol - acid - tannin - sugar)

FLAVOR INTENSITY:
low | moderate | flavorful | powerful

FLAVORS:

FINISH:
short (< 3 sec) | medium (4-5) | long (5-7) | v. long (>8 sec)

CONCLUSION:

STYLE:
traditional | in-between | modern

rating: ☆ ☆ ☆ ☆ ☆

FOOD: **FOOD PAIRING:**

MATCH: perfect | good | neutral | bad

tasting date: location:

tasting partner(s):

wine name:

producer:

region/appellation:

grape varieties:

vintage: alcohol: price:

COLOR DEPTH:
watery | pale | medium | deep | dark

COLOR HUE:
WHITE: greenish | yellow | straw yellow | gold | amber
RED: purplish | ruby | red | garnet | brick | brown
ROSÉ: pink | salmon | orange | copper

CLARITY:
clear | slight haze | cloudy

AROMA INTENSITY:
low | moderate | aromatic | powerful

DEVELOPMENT:
youthful | some age | aged

AROMAS:

DRY/SWEET:
bone dry | dry | off dry | medium sweet | sweet | very sweet

BODY:
very light | light | medium | medium-full | full-bodied | heavy

ACIDITY:
tart | crisp | fresh | smooth | flabby

TANNINS (IF PRESENT):
LEVEL: low | medium | high   TYPE: soft | round | dry | hard

BALANCE:
good | fair | unbalanced (excess: alcohol - acid - tannin - sugar)

FLAVOR INTENSITY:
low | moderate | flavorful | powerful

FLAVORS:

FINISH:
short (< 3 sec) | medium (4-5) | long (5-7) | v. long (>8 sec)

CONCLUSION:

STYLE:
traditional | in-between | modern

rating: ☆ ☆ ☆ ☆ ☆

FOOD: ## FOOD PAIRING:
MATCH: perfect | good | neutral | bad

tasting date: location:

tasting partner(s):

wine name:

producer:

region/appellation:

grape varieties:

vintage: alcohol: price:

COLOR DEPTH:
watery | pale | medium | deep | dark

COLOR HUE:
WHITE: greenish | yellow | straw yellow | gold | amber
RED: purplish | ruby | red | garnet | brick | brown
ROSÉ: pink | salmon | orange | copper

CLARITY:
clear | slight haze | cloudy

AROMA INTENSITY:
low | moderate | aromatic | powerful

DEVELOPMENT:
youthful | some age | aged

AROMAS:

DRY/SWEET:
bone dry | dry | off dry | medium sweet | sweet | very sweet

BODY:
very light | light | medium | medium-full | full-bodied | heavy

ACIDITY:
tart | crisp | fresh | smooth | flabby

TANNINS (IF PRESENT):
LEVEL: low | medium | high   TYPE: soft | round | dry | hard

BALANCE:
good | fair | unbalanced (excess: alcohol - acid - tannin - sugar)

FLAVOR INTENSITY:
low | moderate | flavorful | powerful

FLAVORS:

FINISH:
short (< 3 sec) | medium (4-5) | long (5-7) | v. long (>8 sec)

CONCLUSION:

STYLE:
traditional | in-between | modern

rating: ☆ ☆ ☆ ☆ ☆

FOOD: **FOOD PAIRING:**

            MATCH: perfect | good | neutral | bad

tasting date: location:

tasting partner(s):

wine name:

producer:

region/appellation:

grape varieties:

vintage: alcohol: price:

COLOR DEPTH:
watery | pale | medium | deep | dark

COLOR HUE:
WHITE: greenish | yellow | straw yellow | gold | amber
RED: purplish | ruby | red | garnet | brick | brown
ROSÉ: pink | salmon | orange | copper

CLARITY:
clear | slight haze | cloudy

AROMA INTENSITY:
low | moderate | aromatic | powerful

DEVELOPMENT:
youthful | some age | aged

AROMAS:

DRY/SWEET:
bone dry | dry | off dry | medium sweet | sweet | very sweet

BODY:
very light | light | medium | medium-full | full-bodied | heavy

ACIDITY:
tart | crisp | fresh | smooth | flabby

TANNINS (IF PRESENT):
LEVEL: low | medium | high   TYPE: soft | round | dry | hard

BALANCE:
good | fair | unbalanced (excess: alcohol - acid - tannin - sugar)

FLAVOR INTENSITY:
low | moderate | flavorful | powerful

FLAVORS:

FINISH:
short (< 3 sec) | medium (4-5) | long (5-7) | v. long (>8 sec)

CONCLUSION:

STYLE:
traditional | in-between | modern

rating: ☆ ☆ ☆ ☆ ☆

FOOD: ## FOOD PAIRING:
MATCH: perfect | good | neutral | bad

tasting date: location:

tasting partner(s):

wine name:

producer:

region/appellation:

grape varieties:

vintage: alcohol: price:

COLOR DEPTH:
watery | pale | medium | deep | dark

COLOR HUE:
WHITE: greenish | yellow | straw yellow | gold | amber
RED: purplish | ruby | red | garnet | brick | brown
ROSÉ: pink | salmon | orange | copper

CLARITY:
clear | slight haze | cloudy

AROMA INTENSITY:
low | moderate | aromatic | powerful

DEVELOPMENT:
youthful | some age | aged

AROMAS:

DRY/SWEET:
bone dry | dry | off dry | medium sweet | sweet | very sweet

BODY:
very light | light | medium | medium-full | full-bodied | heavy

ACIDITY:
tart | crisp | fresh | smooth | flabby

TANNINS (IF PRESENT):
LEVEL: low | medium | high   TYPE: soft | round | dry | hard

BALANCE:
good | fair | unbalanced (excess: alcohol - acid - tannin - sugar)

FLAVOR INTENSITY:
low | moderate | flavorful | powerful

FLAVORS:

FINISH:
short (< 3 sec) | medium (4-5) | long (5-7) | v. long (>8 sec)

CONCLUSION:

STYLE:
traditional | in-between | modern

rating: ☆ ☆ ☆ ☆ ☆

FOOD: **FOOD PAIRING:**

MATCH: perfect | good | neutral | bad

tasting date: location:

tasting partner(s):

wine name:

producer:

region/appellation:

grape varieties:

vintage: alcohol: price:

COLOR DEPTH:
watery | pale | medium | deep | dark

COLOR HUE:
WHITE: greenish | yellow | straw yellow | gold | amber
RED: purplish | ruby | red | garnet | brick | brown
ROSÉ: pink | salmon | orange | copper

CLARITY:
clear | slight haze | cloudy

AROMA INTENSITY:
low | moderate | aromatic | powerful

DEVELOPMENT:
youthful | some age | aged

AROMAS:

DRY/SWEET:
bone dry | dry | off dry | medium sweet | sweet | very sweet

BODY:
very light | light | medium | medium-full | full-bodied | heavy

ACIDITY:
tart | crisp | fresh | smooth | flabby

TANNINS (IF PRESENT):
LEVEL: low | medium | high   TYPE: soft | round | dry | hard

BALANCE:
good | fair | unbalanced (excess: alcohol - acid - tannin - sugar)

FLAVOR INTENSITY:
low | moderate | flavorful | powerful

FLAVORS:

FINISH:
short (< 3 sec) | medium (4-5) | long (5-7) | v. long (>8 sec)

CONCLUSION:

STYLE:
traditional | in-between | modern

rating: ☆ ☆ ☆ ☆ ☆

FOOD: **FOOD PAIRING:**

MATCH: perfect | good | neutral | bad

tasting date: location:

tasting partner(s):

wine name:

producer:

region/appellation:

grape varieties:

vintage: alcohol: price:

COLOR DEPTH:
watery | pale | medium | deep | dark

COLOR HUE:
WHITE: greenish | yellow | straw yellow | gold | amber
RED: purplish | ruby | red | garnet | brick | brown
ROSÉ: pink | salmon | orange | copper

CLARITY:
clear | slight haze | cloudy

AROMA INTENSITY:
low | moderate | aromatic | powerful

DEVELOPMENT:
youthful | some age | aged

AROMAS:

DRY/SWEET:
bone dry | dry | off dry | medium sweet | sweet | very sweet

BODY:
very light | light | medium | medium-full | full-bodied | heavy

ACIDITY:
tart | crisp | fresh | smooth | flabby

TANNINS (IF PRESENT):
LEVEL: low | medium | high   TYPE: soft | round | dry | hard

BALANCE:
good | fair | unbalanced (excess: alcohol - acid - tannin - sugar)

FLAVOR INTENSITY:
low | moderate | flavorful | powerful

FLAVORS:

FINISH:
short (< 3 sec) | medium (4-5) | long (5-7) | v. long (>8 sec)

CONCLUSION:

STYLE:
traditional | in-between | modern

rating: ☆ ☆ ☆ ☆ ☆

FOOD: **FOOD PAIRING:**

MATCH: perfect | good | neutral | bad

tasting date: location:

tasting partner(s):

wine name:

producer:

region/appellation:

grape varieties:

vintage: alcohol: price:

COLOR DEPTH:
watery | pale | medium | deep | dark

COLOR HUE:
WHITE: greenish | yellow | straw yellow | gold | amber
RED: purplish | ruby | red | garnet | brick | brown
ROSÉ: pink | salmon | orange | copper

CLARITY:
clear | slight haze | cloudy

AROMA INTENSITY:
low | moderate | aromatic | powerful

DEVELOPMENT:
youthful | some age | aged

AROMAS:

DRY/SWEET:
bone dry | dry | off dry | medium sweet | sweet | very sweet

BODY:
very light | light | medium | medium-full | full-bodied | heavy

ACIDITY:
tart | crisp | fresh | smooth | flabby

TANNINS (IF PRESENT):
LEVEL: low | medium | high   TYPE: soft | round | dry | hard

BALANCE:
good | fair | unbalanced (excess: alcohol - acid - tannin - sugar)

FLAVOR INTENSITY:
low | moderate | flavorful | powerful

FLAVORS:

FINISH:
short (< 3 sec) | medium (4-5) | long (5-7) | v. long (>8 sec)

CONCLUSION:

STYLE:
traditional | in-between | modern

rating: ☆ ☆ ☆ ☆ ☆

FOOD: **FOOD PAIRING:**
                 MATCH: perfect | good | neutral | bad

tasting date: location:

tasting partner(s):

wine name:

producer:

region/appellation:

grape varieties:

vintage: alcohol: price:

COLOR DEPTH:
watery | pale | medium | deep | dark

COLOR HUE:
WHITE: greenish | yellow | straw yellow | gold | amber
RED: purplish | ruby | red | garnet | brick | brown
ROSÉ: pink | salmon | orange | copper

CLARITY:
clear | slight haze | cloudy

AROMA INTENSITY:
low | moderate | aromatic | powerful

DEVELOPMENT:
youthful | some age | aged

AROMAS:

DRY/SWEET:
bone dry | dry | off dry | medium sweet | sweet | very sweet

BODY:
very light | light | medium | medium-full | full-bodied | heavy

ACIDITY:
tart | crisp | fresh | smooth | flabby

TANNINS (IF PRESENT):
LEVEL: low | medium | high   TYPE: soft | round | dry | hard

BALANCE:
good | fair | unbalanced (excess: alcohol - acid - tannin - sugar)

FLAVOR INTENSITY:
low | moderate | flavorful | powerful

FLAVORS:

FINISH:
short (< 3 sec) | medium (4-5) | long (5-7) | v. long (>8 sec)

CONCLUSION:

STYLE:
traditional | in-between | modern

rating: ☆ ☆ ☆ ☆ ☆

FOOD: **FOOD PAIRING:**

MATCH: perfect | good | neutral | bad

tasting date: location:

tasting partner(s):

wine name:

producer:

region/appellation:

grape varieties:

vintage: alcohol: price:

COLOR DEPTH:
watery | pale | medium | deep | dark

COLOR HUE:
WHITE: greenish | yellow | straw yellow | gold | amber
RED: purplish | ruby | red | garnet | brick | brown
ROSÉ: pink | salmon | orange | copper

CLARITY:
clear | slight haze | cloudy

AROMA INTENSITY:
low | moderate | aromatic | powerful

DEVELOPMENT:
youthful | some age | aged

AROMAS:

DRY/SWEET:
bone dry | dry | off dry | medium sweet | sweet | very sweet

BODY:
very light | light | medium | medium-full | full-bodied | heavy

ACIDITY:
tart | crisp | fresh | smooth | flabby

TANNINS (IF PRESENT):
LEVEL: low | medium | high   TYPE: soft | round | dry | hard

BALANCE:
good | fair | unbalanced (excess: alcohol - acid - tannin - sugar)

FLAVOR INTENSITY:
low | moderate | flavorful | powerful

FLAVORS:

FINISH:
short (< 3 sec) | medium (4-5) | long (5-7) | v. long (>8 sec)

CONCLUSION:

STYLE:
traditional | in-between | modern

rating: ☆ ☆ ☆ ☆ ☆

FOOD: **FOOD PAIRING:**
                    MATCH: perfect | good | neutral | bad

tasting date: location:

tasting partner(s):

wine name:

producer:

region/appellation:

grape varieties:

vintage: alcohol: price:

COLOR DEPTH:
watery | pale | medium | deep | dark

COLOR HUE:
WHITE: greenish | yellow | straw yellow | gold | amber
RED: purplish | ruby | red | garnet | brick | brown
ROSÉ: pink | salmon | orange | copper

CLARITY:
clear | slight haze | cloudy

AROMA INTENSITY:
low | moderate | aromatic | powerful

DEVELOPMENT:
youthful | some age | aged

AROMAS:

DRY/SWEET:
bone dry | dry | off dry | medium sweet | sweet | very sweet

BODY:
very light | light | medium | medium-full | full-bodied | heavy

ACIDITY:
tart | crisp | fresh | smooth | flabby

TANNINS (IF PRESENT):
LEVEL: low | medium | high   TYPE: soft | round | dry | hard

BALANCE:
good | fair | unbalanced (excess: alcohol - acid - tannin - sugar)

FLAVOR INTENSITY:
low | moderate | flavorful | powerful

FLAVORS:

FINISH:
short (< 3 sec) | medium (4-5) | long (5-7) | v. long (>8 sec)

CONCLUSION:

STYLE:
traditional | in-between | modern

rating: ☆ ☆ ☆ ☆ ☆

FOOD: **FOOD PAIRING:**

MATCH: perfect | good | neutral | bad

tasting date: location:

tasting partner(s):

wine name:

producer:

region/appellation:

grape varieties:

vintage: alcohol: price:

COLOR DEPTH:
watery | pale | medium | deep | dark
COLOR HUE:
WHITE: greenish | yellow | straw yellow | gold | amber
RED: purplish | ruby | red | garnet | brick | brown
ROSÉ: pink | salmon | orange | copper
CLARITY:
clear | slight haze | cloudy

AROMA INTENSITY:
low | moderate | aromatic | powerful
DEVELOPMENT:
youthful | some age | aged
AROMAS:

DRY/SWEET:
bone dry | dry | off dry | medium sweet | sweet | very sweet
BODY:
very light | light | medium | medium-full | full-bodied | heavy
ACIDITY:
tart | crisp | fresh | smooth | flabby
TANNINS (IF PRESENT):
LEVEL: low | medium | high   TYPE: soft | round | dry | hard
BALANCE:
good | fair | unbalanced (excess: alcohol - acid - tannin - sugar)
FLAVOR INTENSITY:
low | moderate | flavorful | powerful
FLAVORS:

FINISH:
short (< 3 sec) | medium (4-5) | long (5-7) | v. long (>8 sec)
CONCLUSION:

STYLE:
traditional | in-between | modern
rating: ☆ ☆ ☆ ☆ ☆

FOOD: **FOOD PAIRING:**
                MATCH: perfect | good | neutral | bad

tasting date: location:

tasting partner(s):

wine name:

producer:

region/appellation:

grape varieties:

vintage: alcohol: price:

COLOR DEPTH:
watery | pale | medium | deep | dark

COLOR HUE:
WHITE: greenish | yellow | straw yellow | gold | amber
RED: purplish | ruby | red | garnet | brick | brown
ROSÉ: pink | salmon | orange | copper

CLARITY:
clear | slight haze | cloudy

AROMA INTENSITY:
low | moderate | aromatic | powerful

DEVELOPMENT:
youthful | some age | aged

AROMAS:

DRY/SWEET:
bone dry | dry | off dry | medium sweet | sweet | very sweet

BODY:
very light | light | medium | medium-full | full-bodied | heavy

ACIDITY:
tart | crisp | fresh | smooth | flabby

TANNINS (IF PRESENT):
LEVEL: low | medium | high   TYPE: soft | round | dry | hard

BALANCE:
good | fair | unbalanced (excess: alcohol - acid - tannin - sugar)

FLAVOR INTENSITY:
low | moderate | flavorful | powerful

FLAVORS:

FINISH:
short (< 3 sec) | medium (4-5) | long (5-7) | v. long (>8 sec)

CONCLUSION:

STYLE:
traditional | in-between | modern

rating: ☆ ☆ ☆ ☆ ☆

FOOD: **FOOD PAIRING:**

MATCH: perfect | good | neutral | bad

tasting date: location:

tasting partner(s):

wine name:

producer:

region/appellation:

grape varieties:

vintage: alcohol: price:

 COLOR DEPTH:
watery | pale | medium | deep | dark

COLOR HUE:
WHITE: greenish | yellow | straw yellow | gold | amber
RED: purplish | ruby | red | garnet | brick | brown
ROSÉ: pink | salmon | orange | copper

CLARITY:
clear | slight haze | cloudy

AROMA INTENSITY:
low | moderate | aromatic | powerful

DEVELOPMENT:
youthful | some age | aged

AROMAS:

DRY/SWEET:
bone dry | dry | off dry | medium sweet | sweet | very sweet

BODY:
very light | light | medium | medium-full | full-bodied | heavy

ACIDITY:
tart | crisp | fresh | smooth | flabby

TANNINS (IF PRESENT):
LEVEL: low | medium | high   TYPE: soft | round | dry | hard

BALANCE:
good | fair | unbalanced (excess: alcohol - acid - tannin - sugar)

FLAVOR INTENSITY:
low | moderate | flavorful | powerful

FLAVORS:

FINISH:
short (< 3 sec) | medium (4-5) | long (5-7) | v. long (>8 sec)

CONCLUSION:

STYLE:
traditional | in-between | modern

rating: ☆ ☆ ☆ ☆ ☆

FOOD: **FOOD PAIRING:**
MATCH: perfect | good | neutral | bad

tasting date: location:

tasting partner(s):

wine name:

producer:

region/appellation:

grape varieties:

vintage: alcohol: price:

COLOR DEPTH:
watery | pale | medium | deep | dark

COLOR HUE:
WHITE: greenish | yellow | straw yellow | gold | amber
RED: purplish | ruby | red | garnet | brick | brown
ROSÉ: pink | salmon | orange | copper

CLARITY:
clear | slight haze | cloudy

AROMA INTENSITY:
low | moderate | aromatic | powerful

DEVELOPMENT:
youthful | some age | aged

AROMAS:

DRY/SWEET:
bone dry | dry | off dry | medium sweet | sweet | very sweet

BODY:
very light | light | medium | medium-full | full-bodied | heavy

ACIDITY:
tart | crisp | fresh | smooth | flabby

TANNINS (IF PRESENT):
LEVEL: low | medium | high   TYPE: soft | round | dry | hard

BALANCE:
good | fair | unbalanced (excess: alcohol - acid - tannin - sugar)

FLAVOR INTENSITY:
low | moderate | flavorful | powerful

FLAVORS:

FINISH:
short (< 3 sec) | medium (4-5) | long (5-7) | v. long (>8 sec)

CONCLUSION:

STYLE:
traditional | in-between | modern

rating: ☆ ☆ ☆ ☆ ☆

FOOD: **FOOD PAIRING:**

MATCH: perfect | good | neutral | bad

tasting date: location:

tasting partner(s):

wine name:

producer:

region/appellation:

grape varieties:

vintage: alcohol: price:

COLOR DEPTH:
watery | pale | medium | deep | dark

COLOR HUE:
WHITE: greenish | yellow | straw yellow | gold | amber
RED: purplish | ruby | red | garnet | brick | brown
ROSÉ: pink | salmon | orange | copper

CLARITY:
clear | slight haze | cloudy

AROMA INTENSITY:
low | moderate | aromatic | powerful

DEVELOPMENT:
youthful | some age | aged

AROMAS:

DRY/SWEET:
bone dry | dry | off dry | medium sweet | sweet | very sweet

BODY:
very light | light | medium | medium-full | full-bodied | heavy

ACIDITY:
tart | crisp | fresh | smooth | flabby

TANNINS (IF PRESENT):
LEVEL: low | medium | high   TYPE: soft | round | dry | hard

BALANCE:
good | fair | unbalanced (excess: alcohol - acid - tannin - sugar)

FLAVOR INTENSITY:
low | moderate | flavorful | powerful

FLAVORS:

FINISH:
short (< 3 sec) | medium (4-5) | long (5-7) | v. long (>8 sec)

CONCLUSION:

STYLE:
traditional | in-between | modern

rating: ☆ ☆ ☆ ☆ ☆

FOOD: **FOOD PAIRING:**
                   MATCH: perfect | good | neutral | bad

tasting date: location:

tasting partner(s):

wine name:

producer:

region/appellation:

grape varieties:

vintage: alcohol: price:

COLOR DEPTH:
watery | pale | medium | deep | dark

COLOR HUE:
WHITE: greenish | yellow | straw yellow | gold | amber
RED: purplish | ruby | red | garnet | brick | brown
ROSÉ: pink | salmon | orange | copper

CLARITY:
clear | slight haze | cloudy

AROMA INTENSITY:
low | moderate | aromatic | powerful

DEVELOPMENT:
youthful | some age | aged

AROMAS:

DRY/SWEET:
bone dry | dry | off dry | medium sweet | sweet | very sweet

BODY:
very light | light | medium | medium-full | full-bodied | heavy

ACIDITY:
tart | crisp | fresh | smooth | flabby

TANNINS (IF PRESENT):
LEVEL: low | medium | high   TYPE: soft | round | dry | hard

BALANCE:
good | fair | unbalanced (excess: alcohol - acid - tannin - sugar)

FLAVOR INTENSITY:
low | moderate | flavorful | powerful

FLAVORS:

FINISH:
short (< 3 sec) | medium (4-5) | long (5-7) | v. long (>8 sec)

CONCLUSION:

STYLE:
traditional | in-between | modern

rating: ☆ ☆ ☆ ☆ ☆

FOOD: **FOOD PAIRING:**
MATCH: perfect | good | neutral | bad

tasting date: location:

tasting partner(s):

wine name:

producer:

region/appellation:

grape varieties:

vintage: alcohol: price:

COLOR DEPTH:
watery | pale | medium | deep | dark

COLOR HUE:
WHITE: greenish | yellow | straw yellow | gold | amber
RED: purplish | ruby | red | garnet | brick | brown
ROSÉ: pink | salmon | orange | copper

CLARITY:
clear | slight haze | cloudy

AROMA INTENSITY:
low | moderate | aromatic | powerful

DEVELOPMENT:
youthful | some age | aged

AROMAS:

DRY/SWEET:
bone dry | dry | off dry | medium sweet | sweet | very sweet

BODY:
very light | light | medium | medium-full | full-bodied | heavy

ACIDITY:
tart | crisp | fresh | smooth | flabby

TANNINS (IF PRESENT):
LEVEL: low | medium | high   TYPE: soft | round | dry | hard

BALANCE:
good | fair | unbalanced (excess: alcohol - acid - tannin - sugar)

FLAVOR INTENSITY:
low | moderate | flavorful | powerful

FLAVORS:

FINISH:
short (< 3 sec) | medium (4-5) | long (5-7) | v. long (>8 sec)

CONCLUSION:

STYLE:
traditional | in-between | modern

rating: ☆ ☆ ☆ ☆ ☆

FOOD: **FOOD PAIRING:**
                    MATCH: perfect | good | neutral | bad

tasting date: location:

tasting partner(s):

wine name:

producer:

region/appellation:

grape varieties:

vintage: alcohol: price:

 COLOR DEPTH:
watery | pale | medium | deep | dark

COLOR HUE:
WHITE: greenish | yellow | straw yellow | gold | amber
RED: purplish | ruby | red | garnet | brick | brown
ROSÉ: pink | salmon | orange | copper

CLARITY:
clear | slight haze | cloudy

AROMA INTENSITY:
low | moderate | aromatic | powerful

DEVELOPMENT:
youthful | some age | aged

AROMAS:

 DRY/SWEET:
bone dry | dry | off dry | medium sweet | sweet | very sweet

BODY:
very light | light | medium | medium-full | full-bodied | heavy

ACIDITY:
tart | crisp | fresh | smooth | flabby

TANNINS (IF PRESENT):
LEVEL: low | medium | high   TYPE: soft | round | dry | hard

BALANCE:
good | fair | unbalanced (excess: alcohol - acid - tannin - sugar)

FLAVOR INTENSITY:
low | moderate | flavorful | powerful

FLAVORS:

FINISH:
short (< 3 sec) | medium (4-5) | long (5-7) | v. long (>8 sec)

CONCLUSION:

STYLE:
traditional | in-between | modern

rating: ☆ ☆ ☆ ☆ ☆

FOOD: **FOOD PAIRING:**
MATCH: perfect | good | neutral | bad

tasting date: location:

tasting partner(s):

wine name:

producer:

region/appellation:

grape varieties:

vintage: alcohol: price:

COLOR DEPTH:
watery | pale | medium | deep | dark

COLOR HUE:
WHITE: greenish | yellow | straw yellow | gold | amber
RED: purplish | ruby | red | garnet | brick | brown
ROSÉ: pink | salmon | orange | copper

CLARITY:
clear | slight haze | cloudy

AROMA INTENSITY:
low | moderate | aromatic | powerful

DEVELOPMENT:
youthful | some age | aged

AROMAS:

DRY/SWEET:
bone dry | dry | off dry | medium sweet | sweet | very sweet

BODY:
very light | light | medium | medium-full | full-bodied | heavy

ACIDITY:
tart | crisp | fresh | smooth | flabby

TANNINS (IF PRESENT):
LEVEL: low | medium | high   TYPE: soft | round | dry | hard

BALANCE:
good | fair | unbalanced (excess: alcohol - acid - tannin - sugar)

FLAVOR INTENSITY:
low | moderate | flavorful | powerful

FLAVORS:

FINISH:
short (< 3 sec) | medium (4-5) | long (5-7) | v. long (>8 sec)

CONCLUSION:

STYLE:
traditional | in-between | modern

rating: ☆ ☆ ☆ ☆ ☆

FOOD: **FOOD PAIRING:**
MATCH: perfect | good | neutral | bad

tasting date: location:

tasting partner(s):

wine name:

producer:

region/appellation:

grape varieties:

vintage: alcohol: price:

COLOR DEPTH:
watery | pale | medium | deep | dark

COLOR HUE:
WHITE: greenish | yellow | straw yellow | gold | amber
RED: purplish | ruby | red | garnet | brick | brown
ROSÉ: pink | salmon | orange | copper

CLARITY:
clear | slight haze | cloudy

AROMA INTENSITY:
low | moderate | aromatic | powerful

DEVELOPMENT:
youthful | some age | aged

AROMAS:

DRY/SWEET:
bone dry | dry | off dry | medium sweet | sweet | very sweet

BODY:
very light | light | medium | medium-full | full-bodied | heavy

ACIDITY:
tart | crisp | fresh | smooth | flabby

TANNINS (IF PRESENT):
LEVEL: low | medium | high   TYPE: soft | round | dry | hard

BALANCE:
good | fair | unbalanced (excess: alcohol - acid - tannin - sugar)

FLAVOR INTENSITY:
low | moderate | flavorful | powerful

FLAVORS:

FINISH:
short (< 3 sec) | medium (4-5) | long (5-7) | v. long (>8 sec)

CONCLUSION:

STYLE:
traditional | in-between | modern

rating: ☆ ☆ ☆ ☆ ☆

FOOD: **FOOD PAIRING:**

MATCH: perfect | good | neutral | bad

tasting date: location:

tasting partner(s):

wine name:

producer:

region/appellation:

grape varieties:

vintage: alcohol: price:

COLOR DEPTH:
watery | pale | medium | deep | dark

COLOR HUE:
WHITE: greenish | yellow | straw yellow | gold | amber
RED: purplish | ruby | red | garnet | brick | brown
ROSÉ: pink | salmon | orange | copper

CLARITY:
clear | slight haze | cloudy

AROMA INTENSITY:
low | moderate | aromatic | powerful

DEVELOPMENT:
youthful | some age | aged

AROMAS:

DRY/SWEET:
bone dry | dry | off dry | medium sweet | sweet | very sweet

BODY:
very light | light | medium | medium-full | full-bodied | heavy

ACIDITY:
tart | crisp | fresh | smooth | flabby

TANNINS (IF PRESENT):
LEVEL: low | medium | high   TYPE: soft | round | dry | hard

BALANCE:
good | fair | unbalanced (excess: alcohol - acid - tannin - sugar)

FLAVOR INTENSITY:
low | moderate | flavorful | powerful

FLAVORS:

FINISH:
short (< 3 sec) | medium (4-5) | long (5-7) | v. long (>8 sec)

CONCLUSION:

STYLE:
traditional | in-between | modern

rating: ☆ ☆ ☆ ☆ ☆

FOOD: ## FOOD PAIRING:
MATCH: perfect | good | neutral | bad

tasting date: location:

tasting partner(s):

wine name:

producer:

region/appellation:

grape varieties:

vintage: alcohol: price:

COLOR DEPTH:
watery | pale | medium | deep | dark

COLOR HUE:
WHITE: greenish | yellow | straw yellow | gold | amber
RED: purplish | ruby | red | garnet | brick | brown
ROSÉ: pink | salmon | orange | copper

CLARITY:
clear | slight haze | cloudy

AROMA INTENSITY:
low | moderate | aromatic | powerful

DEVELOPMENT:
youthful | some age | aged

AROMAS:

DRY/SWEET:
bone dry | dry | off dry | medium sweet | sweet | very sweet

BODY:
very light | light | medium | medium-full | full-bodied | heavy

ACIDITY:
tart | crisp | fresh | smooth | flabby

TANNINS (IF PRESENT):
LEVEL: low | medium | high   TYPE: soft | round | dry | hard

BALANCE:
good | fair | unbalanced (excess: alcohol - acid - tannin - sugar)

FLAVOR INTENSITY:
low | moderate | flavorful | powerful

FLAVORS:

FINISH:
short (< 3 sec) | medium (4-5) | long (5-7) | v. long (>8 sec)

CONCLUSION:

STYLE:
traditional | in-between | modern

rating: ☆ ☆ ☆ ☆ ☆

FOOD: **FOOD PAIRING:**

MATCH: perfect | good | neutral | bad

tasting date: location:

tasting partner(s):

wine name:

producer:

region/appellation:

grape varieties:

vintage: alcohol: price:

COLOR DEPTH:
watery | pale | medium | deep | dark

COLOR HUE:
WHITE: greenish | yellow | straw yellow | gold | amber
RED: purplish | ruby | red | garnet | brick | brown
ROSÉ: pink | salmon | orange | copper

CLARITY:
clear | slight haze | cloudy

AROMA INTENSITY:
low | moderate | aromatic | powerful

DEVELOPMENT:
youthful | some age | aged

AROMAS:

DRY/SWEET:
bone dry | dry | off dry | medium sweet | sweet | very sweet

BODY:
very light | light | medium | medium-full | full-bodied | heavy

ACIDITY:
tart | crisp | fresh | smooth | flabby

TANNINS (IF PRESENT):
LEVEL: low | medium | high   TYPE: soft | round | dry | hard

BALANCE:
good | fair | unbalanced (excess: alcohol - acid - tannin - sugar)

FLAVOR INTENSITY:
low | moderate | flavorful | powerful

FLAVORS:

FINISH:
short (< 3 sec) | medium (4-5) | long (5-7) | v. long (>8 sec)

CONCLUSION:

STYLE:
traditional | in-between | modern

rating: ☆ ☆ ☆ ☆ ☆

FOOD: **FOOD PAIRING:**
                MATCH: perfect | good | neutral | bad

tasting date: location:

tasting partner(s):

wine name:

producer:

region/appellation:

grape varieties:

vintage: alcohol: price:

COLOR DEPTH:
watery | pale | medium | deep | dark

COLOR HUE:
WHITE: greenish | yellow | straw yellow | gold | amber
RED: purplish | ruby | red | garnet | brick | brown
ROSÉ: pink | salmon | orange | copper

CLARITY:
clear | slight haze | cloudy

AROMA INTENSITY:
low | moderate | aromatic | powerful

DEVELOPMENT:
youthful | some age | aged

AROMAS:

DRY/SWEET:
bone dry | dry | off dry | medium sweet | sweet | very sweet

BODY:
very light | light | medium | medium-full | full-bodied | heavy

ACIDITY:
tart | crisp | fresh | smooth | flabby

TANNINS (IF PRESENT):
LEVEL: low | medium | high   TYPE: soft | round | dry | hard

BALANCE:
good | fair | unbalanced (excess: alcohol - acid - tannin - sugar)

FLAVOR INTENSITY:
low | moderate | flavorful | powerful

FLAVORS:

FINISH:
short (< 3 sec) | medium (4-5) | long (5-7) | v. long (>8 sec)

CONCLUSION:

STYLE:
traditional | in-between | modern

rating: ☆ ☆ ☆ ☆ ☆

FOOD: **FOOD PAIRING:**
                   MATCH: perfect | good | neutral | bad

tasting date: location:

tasting partner(s):

wine name:

producer:

region/appellation:

grape varieties:

vintage: alcohol: price:

COLOR DEPTH:
watery | pale | medium | deep | dark

COLOR HUE:
WHITE: greenish | yellow | straw yellow | gold | amber
RED: purplish | ruby | red | garnet | brick | brown
ROSÉ: pink | salmon | orange | copper

CLARITY:
clear | slight haze | cloudy

AROMA INTENSITY:
low | moderate | aromatic | powerful

DEVELOPMENT:
youthful | some age | aged

AROMAS:

DRY/SWEET:
bone dry | dry | off dry | medium sweet | sweet | very sweet

BODY:
very light | light | medium | medium-full | full-bodied | heavy

ACIDITY:
tart | crisp | fresh | smooth | flabby

TANNINS (IF PRESENT):
LEVEL: low | medium | high   TYPE: soft | round | dry | hard

BALANCE:
good | fair | unbalanced (excess: alcohol - acid - tannin - sugar)

FLAVOR INTENSITY:
low | moderate | flavorful | powerful

FLAVORS:

FINISH:
short (< 3 sec) | medium (4-5) | long (5-7) | v. long (>8 sec)

CONCLUSION:

STYLE:
traditional | in-between | modern

rating: ☆ ☆ ☆ ☆ ☆

FOOD: ### FOOD PAIRING:
MATCH: perfect | good | neutral | bad

tasting date: location:

tasting partner(s):

wine name:

producer:

region/appellation:

grape varieties:

vintage: alcohol: price:

COLOR DEPTH:
watery | pale | medium | deep | dark

COLOR HUE:
WHITE: greenish | yellow | straw yellow | gold | amber
RED: purplish | ruby | red | garnet | brick | brown
ROSÉ: pink | salmon | orange | copper

CLARITY:
clear | slight haze | cloudy

AROMA INTENSITY:
low | moderate | aromatic | powerful

DEVELOPMENT:
youthful | some age | aged

AROMAS:

DRY/SWEET:
bone dry | dry | off dry | medium sweet | sweet | very sweet

BODY:
very light | light | medium | medium-full | full-bodied | heavy

ACIDITY:
tart | crisp | fresh | smooth | flabby

TANNINS (IF PRESENT):
LEVEL: low | medium | high   TYPE: soft | round | dry | hard

BALANCE:
good | fair | unbalanced (excess: alcohol - acid - tannin - sugar)

FLAVOR INTENSITY:
low | moderate | flavorful | powerful

FLAVORS:

FINISH:
short (< 3 sec) | medium (4-5) | long (5-7) | v. long (>8 sec)

CONCLUSION:

STYLE:
traditional | in-between | modern

rating: ☆ ☆ ☆ ☆ ☆

FOOD: **FOOD PAIRING:**

MATCH: perfect | good | neutral | bad

tasting date: location:

tasting partner(s):

wine name:

producer:

region/appellation:

grape varieties:

vintage: alcohol: price:

COLOR DEPTH:
watery | pale | medium | deep | dark

COLOR HUE:
WHITE: greenish | yellow | straw yellow | gold | amber
RED: purplish | ruby | red | garnet | brick | brown
ROSÉ: pink | salmon | orange | copper

CLARITY:
clear | slight haze | cloudy

AROMA INTENSITY:
low | moderate | aromatic | powerful

DEVELOPMENT:
youthful | some age | aged

AROMAS:

DRY/SWEET:
bone dry | dry | off dry | medium sweet | sweet | very sweet

BODY:
very light | light | medium | medium-full | full-bodied | heavy

ACIDITY:
tart | crisp | fresh | smooth | flabby

TANNINS (IF PRESENT):
LEVEL: low | medium | high   TYPE: soft | round | dry | hard

BALANCE:
good | fair | unbalanced (excess: alcohol - acid - tannin - sugar)

FLAVOR INTENSITY:
low | moderate | flavorful | powerful

FLAVORS:

FINISH:
short (< 3 sec) | medium (4-5) | long (5-7) | v. long (>8 sec)

CONCLUSION:

STYLE:
traditional | in-between | modern

rating: ☆ ☆ ☆ ☆ ☆

FOOD: ## FOOD PAIRING:
                   MATCH: perfect | good | neutral | bad

tasting date: location:

tasting partner(s):

wine name:

producer:

region/appellation:

grape varieties:

vintage: alcohol: price:

COLOR DEPTH:
watery | pale | medium | deep | dark

COLOR HUE:
WHITE: greenish | yellow | straw yellow | gold | amber
RED: purplish | ruby | red | garnet | brick | brown
ROSÉ: pink | salmon | orange | copper

CLARITY:
clear | slight haze | cloudy

AROMA INTENSITY:
low | moderate | aromatic | powerful

DEVELOPMENT:
youthful | some age | aged

AROMAS:

DRY/SWEET:
bone dry | dry | off dry | medium sweet | sweet | very sweet

BODY:
very light | light | medium | medium-full | full-bodied | heavy

ACIDITY:
tart | crisp | fresh | smooth | flabby

TANNINS (IF PRESENT):
LEVEL: low | medium | high   TYPE: soft | round | dry | hard

BALANCE:
good | fair | unbalanced (excess: alcohol - acid - tannin - sugar)

FLAVOR INTENSITY:
low | moderate | flavorful | powerful

FLAVORS:

FINISH:
short (< 3 sec) | medium (4-5) | long (5-7) | v. long (>8 sec)

CONCLUSION:

STYLE:
traditional | in-between | modern

rating: ☆ ☆ ☆ ☆ ☆

FOOD: **FOOD PAIRING:**
                MATCH: perfect | good | neutral | bad

tasting date: location:

tasting partner(s):

wine name:

producer:

region/appellation:

grape varieties:

vintage: alcohol: price:

COLOR DEPTH:
watery | pale | medium | deep | dark

COLOR HUE:
WHITE: greenish | yellow | straw yellow | gold | amber
RED: purplish | ruby | red | garnet | brick | brown
ROSÉ: pink | salmon | orange | copper

CLARITY:
clear | slight haze | cloudy

AROMA INTENSITY:
low | moderate | aromatic | powerful

DEVELOPMENT:
youthful | some age | aged

AROMAS:

DRY/SWEET:
bone dry | dry | off dry | medium sweet | sweet | very sweet

BODY:
very light | light | medium | medium-full | full-bodied | heavy

ACIDITY:
tart | crisp | fresh | smooth | flabby

TANNINS (IF PRESENT):
LEVEL: low | medium | high   TYPE: soft | round | dry | hard

BALANCE:
good | fair | unbalanced (excess: alcohol - acid - tannin - sugar)

FLAVOR INTENSITY:
low | moderate | flavorful | powerful

FLAVORS:

FINISH:
short (< 3 sec) | medium (4-5) | long (5-7) | v. long (>8 sec)

CONCLUSION:

STYLE:
traditional | in-between | modern

rating: ☆ ☆ ☆ ☆ ☆

FOOD: **FOOD PAIRING:**
                    MATCH: perfect | good | neutral | bad

tasting date: location:

tasting partner(s):

wine name:

producer:

region/appellation:

grape varieties:

vintage: alcohol: price:

COLOR DEPTH:
watery | pale | medium | deep | dark

COLOR HUE:
WHITE: greenish | yellow | straw yellow | gold | amber
RED: purplish | ruby | red | garnet | brick | brown
ROSÉ: pink | salmon | orange | copper

CLARITY:
clear | slight haze | cloudy

AROMA INTENSITY:
low | moderate | aromatic | powerful

DEVELOPMENT:
youthful | some age | aged

AROMAS:

DRY/SWEET:
bone dry | dry | off dry | medium sweet | sweet | very sweet

BODY:
very light | light | medium | medium-full | full-bodied | heavy

ACIDITY:
tart | crisp | fresh | smooth | flabby

TANNINS (IF PRESENT):
LEVEL: low | medium | high   TYPE: soft | round | dry | hard

BALANCE:
good | fair | unbalanced (excess: alcohol - acid - tannin - sugar)

FLAVOR INTENSITY:
low | moderate | flavorful | powerful

FLAVORS:

FINISH:
short (< 3 sec) | medium (4-5) | long (5-7) | v. long (>8 sec)

CONCLUSION:

STYLE:
traditional | in-between | modern

rating: ☆ ☆ ☆ ☆ ☆

FOOD: ## FOOD PAIRING:
MATCH: perfect | good | neutral | bad

tasting date: location:

tasting partner(s):

wine name:

producer:

region/appellation:

grape varieties:

vintage: alcohol: price:

COLOR DEPTH:
watery | pale | medium | deep | dark

COLOR HUE:
WHITE: greenish | yellow | straw yellow | gold | amber
RED: purplish | ruby | red | garnet | brick | brown
ROSÉ: pink | salmon | orange | copper

CLARITY:
clear | slight haze | cloudy

AROMA INTENSITY:
low | moderate | aromatic | powerful

DEVELOPMENT:
youthful | some age | aged

AROMAS:

DRY/SWEET:
bone dry | dry | off dry | medium sweet | sweet | very sweet

BODY:
very light | light | medium | medium-full | full-bodied | heavy

ACIDITY:
tart | crisp | fresh | smooth | flabby

TANNINS (IF PRESENT):
LEVEL: low | medium | high   TYPE: soft | round | dry | hard

BALANCE:
good | fair | unbalanced (excess: alcohol - acid - tannin - sugar)

FLAVOR INTENSITY:
low | moderate | flavorful | powerful

FLAVORS:

FINISH:
short (< 3 sec) | medium (4-5) | long (5-7) | v. long (>8 sec)

CONCLUSION:

STYLE:
traditional | in-between | modern

rating: ☆ ☆ ☆ ☆ ☆

FOOD: **FOOD PAIRING:**
                 MATCH: perfect | good | neutral | bad

tasting date: location:

tasting partner(s):

wine name:

producer:

region/appellation:

grape varieties:

vintage: alcohol: price:

COLOR DEPTH:
watery | pale | medium | deep | dark

COLOR HUE:
WHITE: greenish | yellow | straw yellow | gold | amber
RED: purplish | ruby | red | garnet | brick | brown
ROSÉ: pink | salmon | orange | copper

CLARITY:
clear | slight haze | cloudy

AROMA INTENSITY:
low | moderate | aromatic | powerful

DEVELOPMENT:
youthful | some age | aged

AROMAS:

DRY/SWEET:
bone dry | dry | off dry | medium sweet | sweet | very sweet

BODY:
very light | light | medium | medium-full | full-bodied | heavy

ACIDITY:
tart | crisp | fresh | smooth | flabby

TANNINS (IF PRESENT):
LEVEL: low | medium | high TYPE: soft | round | dry | hard

BALANCE:
good | fair | unbalanced (excess: alcohol - acid - tannin - sugar)

FLAVOR INTENSITY:
low | moderate | flavorful | powerful

FLAVORS:

FINISH:
short (< 3 sec) | medium (4-5) | long (5-7) | v. long (>8 sec)

CONCLUSION:

STYLE:
traditional | in-between | modern

rating: ☆ ☆ ☆ ☆ ☆

FOOD: ### FOOD PAIRING:
MATCH: perfect | good | neutral | bad

tasting date: location:

tasting partner(s):

wine name:

producer:

region/appellation:

grape varieties:

vintage: alcohol: price:

COLOR DEPTH:
watery | pale | medium | deep | dark

COLOR HUE:
WHITE: greenish | yellow | straw yellow | gold | amber
RED: purplish | ruby | red | garnet | brick | brown
ROSÉ: pink | salmon | orange | copper

CLARITY:
clear | slight haze | cloudy

AROMA INTENSITY:
low | moderate | aromatic | powerful

DEVELOPMENT:
youthful | some age | aged

AROMAS:

DRY/SWEET:
bone dry | dry | off dry | medium sweet | sweet | very sweet

BODY:
very light | light | medium | medium-full | full-bodied | heavy

ACIDITY:
tart | crisp | fresh | smooth | flabby

TANNINS (IF PRESENT):
LEVEL: low | medium | high   TYPE: soft | round | dry | hard

BALANCE:
good | fair | unbalanced (excess: alcohol - acid - tannin - sugar)

FLAVOR INTENSITY:
low | moderate | flavorful | powerful

FLAVORS:

FINISH:
short (< 3 sec) | medium (4-5) | long (5-7) | v. long (>8 sec)

CONCLUSION:

STYLE:
traditional | in-between | modern

rating: ☆ ☆ ☆ ☆ ☆

FOOD: **FOOD PAIRING:**
              MATCH: perfect | good | neutral | bad

tasting date: location:

tasting partner(s):

wine name:

producer:

region/appellation:

grape varieties:

vintage: alcohol: price:

COLOR DEPTH:
watery | pale | medium | deep | dark

COLOR HUE:
WHITE: greenish | yellow | straw yellow | gold | amber
RED: purplish | ruby | red | garnet | brick | brown
ROSÉ: pink | salmon | orange | copper

CLARITY:
clear | slight haze | cloudy

AROMA INTENSITY:
low | moderate | aromatic | powerful

DEVELOPMENT:
youthful | some age | aged

AROMAS:

DRY/SWEET:
bone dry | dry | off dry | medium sweet | sweet | very sweet

BODY:
very light | light | medium | medium-full | full-bodied | heavy

ACIDITY:
tart | crisp | fresh | smooth | flabby

TANNINS (IF PRESENT):
LEVEL: low | medium | high   TYPE: soft | round | dry | hard

BALANCE:
good | fair | unbalanced (excess: alcohol - acid - tannin - sugar)

FLAVOR INTENSITY:
low | moderate | flavorful | powerful

FLAVORS:

FINISH:
short (< 3 sec) | medium (4-5) | long (5-7) | v. long (>8 sec)

CONCLUSION:

STYLE:
traditional | in-between | modern

rating: ☆ ☆ ☆ ☆ ☆

FOOD: **FOOD PAIRING:**

MATCH: perfect | good | neutral | bad

tasting date: location:

tasting partner(s):

wine name:

producer:

region/appellation:

grape varieties:

vintage: alcohol: price:

COLOR DEPTH:
watery | pale | medium | deep | dark

COLOR HUE:
WHITE: greenish | yellow | straw yellow | gold | amber
RED: purplish | ruby | red | garnet | brick | brown
ROSÉ: pink | salmon | orange | copper

CLARITY:
clear | slight haze | cloudy

AROMA INTENSITY:
low | moderate | aromatic | powerful

DEVELOPMENT:
youthful | some age | aged

AROMAS:

DRY/SWEET:
bone dry | dry | off dry | medium sweet | sweet | very sweet

BODY:
very light | light | medium | medium-full | full-bodied | heavy

ACIDITY:
tart | crisp | fresh | smooth | flabby

TANNINS (IF PRESENT):
LEVEL: low | medium | high   TYPE: soft | round | dry | hard

BALANCE:
good | fair | unbalanced (excess: alcohol - acid - tannin - sugar)

FLAVOR INTENSITY:
low | moderate | flavorful | powerful

FLAVORS:

FINISH:
short (< 3 sec) | medium (4-5) | long (5-7) | v. long (>8 sec)

CONCLUSION:

STYLE:
traditional | in-between | modern

rating: ☆ ☆ ☆ ☆ ☆

FOOD: **FOOD PAIRING:**
                MATCH: perfect | good | neutral | bad

tasting date: location:

tasting partner(s):

wine name:

producer:

region/appellation:

grape varieties:

vintage: alcohol: price:

COLOR DEPTH:
watery | pale | medium | deep | dark

COLOR HUE:
WHITE: greenish | yellow | straw yellow | gold | amber
RED: purplish | ruby | red | garnet | brick | brown
ROSÉ: pink | salmon | orange | copper

CLARITY:
clear | slight haze | cloudy

AROMA INTENSITY:
low | moderate | aromatic | powerful

DEVELOPMENT:
youthful | some age | aged

AROMAS:

DRY/SWEET:
bone dry | dry | off dry | medium sweet | sweet | very sweet

BODY:
very light | light | medium | medium-full | full-bodied | heavy

ACIDITY:
tart | crisp | fresh | smooth | flabby

TANNINS (IF PRESENT):
LEVEL: low | medium | high   TYPE: soft | round | dry | hard

BALANCE:
good | fair | unbalanced (excess: alcohol - acid - tannin - sugar)

FLAVOR INTENSITY:
low | moderate | flavorful | powerful

FLAVORS:

FINISH:
short (< 3 sec) | medium (4-5) | long (5-7) | v. long (>8 sec)

CONCLUSION:

STYLE:
traditional | in-between | modern

rating: ☆ ☆ ☆ ☆ ☆

FOOD: **FOOD PAIRING:**
                  MATCH: perfect | good | neutral | bad

tasting date: location:

tasting partner(s):

wine name:

producer:

region/appellation:

grape varieties:

vintage: alcohol: price:

COLOR DEPTH:
watery | pale | medium | deep | dark

COLOR HUE:
WHITE: greenish | yellow | straw yellow | gold | amber
RED: purplish | ruby | red | garnet | brick | brown
ROSÉ: pink | salmon | orange | copper

CLARITY:
clear | slight haze | cloudy

AROMA INTENSITY:
low | moderate | aromatic | powerful

DEVELOPMENT:
youthful | some age | aged

AROMAS:

DRY/SWEET:
bone dry | dry | off dry | medium sweet | sweet | very sweet

BODY:
very light | light | medium | medium-full | full-bodied | heavy

ACIDITY:
tart | crisp | fresh | smooth | flabby

TANNINS (IF PRESENT):
LEVEL: low | medium | high   TYPE: soft | round | dry | hard

BALANCE:
good | fair | unbalanced (excess: alcohol - acid - tannin - sugar)

FLAVOR INTENSITY:
low | moderate | flavorful | powerful

FLAVORS:

FINISH:
short (< 3 sec) | medium (4-5) | long (5-7) | v. long (>8 sec)

CONCLUSION:

STYLE:
traditional | in-between | modern

rating: ☆ ☆ ☆ ☆ ☆

FOOD: **FOOD PAIRING:**
MATCH: perfect | good | neutral | bad

tasting date: location:

tasting partner(s):

wine name:

producer:

region/appellation:

grape varieties:

vintage: alcohol: price:

COLOR DEPTH:
watery | pale | medium | deep | dark

COLOR HUE:
WHITE: greenish | yellow | straw yellow | gold | amber
RED: purplish | ruby | red | garnet | brick | brown
ROSÉ: pink | salmon | orange | copper

CLARITY:
clear | slight haze | cloudy

AROMA INTENSITY:
low | moderate | aromatic | powerful

DEVELOPMENT:
youthful | some age | aged

AROMAS:

DRY/SWEET:
bone dry | dry | off dry | medium sweet | sweet | very sweet

BODY:
very light | light | medium | medium-full | full-bodied | heavy

ACIDITY:
tart | crisp | fresh | smooth | flabby

TANNINS (IF PRESENT):
LEVEL: low | medium | high   TYPE: soft | round | dry | hard

BALANCE:
good | fair | unbalanced (excess: alcohol - acid - tannin - sugar)

FLAVOR INTENSITY:
low | moderate | flavorful | powerful

FLAVORS:

FINISH:
short (< 3 sec) | medium (4-5) | long (5-7) | v. long (>8 sec)

CONCLUSION:

STYLE:
traditional | in-between | modern

rating: ☆ ☆ ☆ ☆ ☆

FOOD: **FOOD PAIRING:**

MATCH: perfect | good | neutral | bad

tasting date: location:

tasting partner(s):

wine name:

producer:

region/appellation:

grape varieties:

vintage: alcohol: price:

COLOR DEPTH:
watery | pale | medium | deep | dark

COLOR HUE:
WHITE: greenish | yellow | straw yellow | gold | amber
RED: purplish | ruby | red | garnet | brick | brown
ROSÉ: pink | salmon | orange | copper

CLARITY:
clear | slight haze | cloudy

AROMA INTENSITY:
low | moderate | aromatic | powerful

DEVELOPMENT:
youthful | some age | aged

AROMAS:

DRY/SWEET:
bone dry | dry | off dry | medium sweet | sweet | very sweet

BODY:
very light | light | medium | medium-full | full-bodied | heavy

ACIDITY:
tart | crisp | fresh | smooth | flabby

TANNINS (IF PRESENT):
LEVEL: low | medium | high   TYPE: soft | round | dry | hard

BALANCE:
good | fair | unbalanced (excess: alcohol - acid - tannin - sugar)

FLAVOR INTENSITY:
low | moderate | flavorful | powerful

FLAVORS:

FINISH:
short (< 3 sec) | medium (4-5) | long (5-7) | v. long (>8 sec)

CONCLUSION:

STYLE:
traditional | in-between | modern

rating: ☆ ☆ ☆ ☆ ☆

FOOD: **FOOD PAIRING:**
              MATCH: perfect | good | neutral | bad

tasting date: location:

tasting partner(s):

wine name:

producer:

region/appellation:

grape varieties:

vintage: alcohol: price:

COLOR DEPTH:
watery | pale | medium | deep | dark

COLOR HUE:
WHITE: greenish | yellow | straw yellow | gold | amber
RED: purplish | ruby | red | garnet | brick | brown
ROSÉ: pink | salmon | orange | copper

CLARITY:
clear | slight haze | cloudy

AROMA INTENSITY:
low | moderate | aromatic | powerful

DEVELOPMENT:
youthful | some age | aged

AROMAS:

DRY/SWEET:
bone dry | dry | off dry | medium sweet | sweet | very sweet

BODY:
very light | light | medium | medium-full | full-bodied | heavy

ACIDITY:
tart | crisp | fresh | smooth | flabby

TANNINS (IF PRESENT):
LEVEL: low | medium | high   TYPE: soft | round | dry | hard

BALANCE:
good | fair | unbalanced (excess: alcohol - acid - tannin - sugar)

FLAVOR INTENSITY:
low | moderate | flavorful | powerful

FLAVORS:

FINISH:
short (< 3 sec) | medium (4-5) | long (5-7) | v. long (>8 sec)

CONCLUSION:

STYLE:
traditional | in-between | modern

rating: ☆ ☆ ☆ ☆ ☆

FOOD: **FOOD PAIRING:**

MATCH: perfect | good | neutral | bad

tasting date: location:

tasting partner(s):

wine name:

producer:

region/appellation:

grape varieties:

vintage: alcohol: price:

COLOR DEPTH:
watery | pale | medium | deep | dark

COLOR HUE:
WHITE: greenish | yellow | straw yellow | gold | amber
RED: purplish | ruby | red | garnet | brick | brown
ROSÉ: pink | salmon | orange | copper

CLARITY:
clear | slight haze | cloudy

AROMA INTENSITY:
low | moderate | aromatic | powerful

DEVELOPMENT:
youthful | some age | aged

AROMAS:

DRY/SWEET:
bone dry | dry | off dry | medium sweet | sweet | very sweet

BODY:
very light | light | medium | medium-full | full-bodied | heavy

ACIDITY:
tart | crisp | fresh | smooth | flabby

TANNINS (IF PRESENT):
LEVEL: low | medium | high   TYPE: soft | round | dry | hard

BALANCE:
good | fair | unbalanced (excess: alcohol - acid - tannin - sugar)

FLAVOR INTENSITY:
low | moderate | flavorful | powerful

FLAVORS:

FINISH:
short (< 3 sec) | medium (4-5) | long (5-7) | v. long (>8 sec)

CONCLUSION:

STYLE:
traditional | in-between | modern

rating: ☆ ☆ ☆ ☆ ☆

FOOD: **FOOD PAIRING:**
MATCH: perfect | good | neutral | bad

tasting date: location:

tasting partner(s):

wine name:

producer:

region/appellation:

grape varieties:

vintage: alcohol: price:

COLOR DEPTH:
watery | pale | medium | deep | dark

COLOR HUE:
WHITE: greenish | yellow | straw yellow | gold | amber
RED: purplish | ruby | red | garnet | brick | brown
ROSÉ: pink | salmon | orange | copper

CLARITY:
clear | slight haze | cloudy

AROMA INTENSITY:
low | moderate | aromatic | powerful

DEVELOPMENT:
youthful | some age | aged

AROMAS:

DRY/SWEET:
bone dry | dry | off dry | medium sweet | sweet | very sweet

BODY:
very light | light | medium | medium-full | full-bodied | heavy

ACIDITY:
tart | crisp | fresh | smooth | flabby

TANNINS (IF PRESENT):
LEVEL: low | medium | high   TYPE: soft | round | dry | hard

BALANCE:
good | fair | unbalanced (excess: alcohol - acid - tannin - sugar)

FLAVOR INTENSITY:
low | moderate | flavorful | powerful

FLAVORS:

FINISH:
short (< 3 sec) | medium (4-5) | long (5-7) | v. long (>8 sec)

CONCLUSION:

STYLE:
traditional | in-between | modern

rating: ☆ ☆ ☆ ☆ ☆

FOOD: **FOOD PAIRING:**

MATCH: perfect | good | neutral | bad

tasting date: location:

tasting partner(s):

wine name:

producer:

region/appellation:

grape varieties: .

vintage: alcohol: price:

COLOR DEPTH:
watery | pale | medium | deep | dark

COLOR HUE:
WHITE: greenish | yellow | straw yellow | gold | amber
RED: purplish | ruby | red | garnet | brick | brown
ROSÉ: pink | salmon | orange | copper

CLARITY:
clear | slight haze | cloudy

AROMA INTENSITY:
low | moderate | aromatic | powerful

DEVELOPMENT:
youthful | some age | aged

AROMAS:

DRY/SWEET:
bone dry | dry | off dry | medium sweet | sweet | very sweet

BODY:
very light | light | medium | medium-full | full-bodied | heavy

ACIDITY:
tart | crisp | fresh | smooth | flabby

TANNINS (IF PRESENT):
LEVEL: low | medium | high   TYPE: soft | round | dry | hard

BALANCE:
good | fair | unbalanced (excess: alcohol - acid - tannin - sugar)

FLAVOR INTENSITY:
low | moderate | flavorful | powerful

FLAVORS:

FINISH:
short (< 3 sec) | medium (4-5) | long (5-7) | v. long (>8 sec)

CONCLUSION:

STYLE:
traditional | in-between | modern

rating: ☆ ☆ ☆ ☆ ☆

FOOD: ### FOOD PAIRING:
MATCH: perfect | good | neutral | bad

tasting date: location:

tasting partner(s):

wine name:

producer:

region/appellation:

grape varieties:

vintage: alcohol: price:

COLOR DEPTH:
watery | pale | medium | deep | dark

COLOR HUE:
WHITE: greenish | yellow | straw yellow | gold | amber
RED: purplish | ruby | red | garnet | brick | brown
ROSÉ: pink | salmon | orange | copper

CLARITY:
clear | slight haze | cloudy

AROMA INTENSITY:
low | moderate | aromatic | powerful

DEVELOPMENT:
youthful | some age | aged

AROMAS:

DRY/SWEET:
bone dry | dry | off dry | medium sweet | sweet | very sweet

BODY:
very light | light | medium | medium-full | full-bodied | heavy

ACIDITY:
tart | crisp | fresh | smooth | flabby

TANNINS (IF PRESENT):
LEVEL: low | medium | high   TYPE: soft | round | dry | hard

BALANCE:
good | fair | unbalanced (excess: alcohol - acid - tannin - sugar)

FLAVOR INTENSITY:
low | moderate | flavorful | powerful

FLAVORS:

FINISH:
short (< 3 sec) | medium (4-5) | long (5-7) | v. long (>8 sec)

CONCLUSION:

STYLE:
traditional | in-between | modern

rating: ☆ ☆ ☆ ☆ ☆

FOOD: **FOOD PAIRING:**

MATCH: perfect | good | neutral | bad

tasting date: location:

tasting partner(s):

wine name:

producer:

region/appellation:

grape varieties:

vintage: alcohol: price:

COLOR DEPTH:
watery | pale | medium | deep | dark

COLOR HUE:
WHITE: greenish | yellow | straw yellow | gold | amber
RED: purplish | ruby | red | garnet | brick | brown
ROSÉ: pink | salmon | orange | copper

CLARITY:
clear | slight haze | cloudy

AROMA INTENSITY:
low | moderate | aromatic | powerful

DEVELOPMENT:
youthful | some age | aged

AROMAS:

DRY/SWEET:
bone dry | dry | off dry | medium sweet | sweet | very sweet

BODY:
very light | light | medium | medium-full | full-bodied | heavy

ACIDITY:
tart | crisp | fresh | smooth | flabby

TANNINS (IF PRESENT):
LEVEL: low | medium | high   TYPE: soft | round | dry | hard

BALANCE:
good | fair | unbalanced (excess: alcohol - acid - tannin - sugar)

FLAVOR INTENSITY:
low | moderate | flavorful | powerful

FLAVORS:

FINISH:
short (< 3 sec) | medium (4-5) | long (5-7) | v. long (>8 sec)

CONCLUSION:

STYLE:
traditional | in-between | modern

rating: ☆ ☆ ☆ ☆ ☆

FOOD: ### FOOD PAIRING:
MATCH: perfect | good | neutral | bad

tasting date: location:

tasting partner(s):

wine name:

producer:

region/appellation:

grape varieties:

vintage: alcohol: price:

COLOR DEPTH:
watery | pale | medium | deep | dark
COLOR HUE:
WHITE: greenish | yellow | straw yellow | gold | amber
RED: purplish | ruby | red | garnet | brick | brown
ROSÉ: pink | salmon | orange | copper
CLARITY:
clear | slight haze | cloudy

AROMA INTENSITY:
low | moderate | aromatic | powerful
DEVELOPMENT:
youthful | some age | aged
AROMAS:

DRY/SWEET:
bone dry | dry | off dry | medium sweet | sweet | very sweet
BODY:
very light | light | medium | medium-full | full-bodied | heavy
ACIDITY:
tart | crisp | fresh | smooth | flabby
TANNINS (IF PRESENT):
LEVEL: low | medium | high   TYPE: soft | round | dry | hard
BALANCE:
good | fair | unbalanced (excess: alcohol - acid - tannin - sugar)
FLAVOR INTENSITY:
low | moderate | flavorful | powerful
FLAVORS:

FINISH:
short (< 3 sec) | medium (4-5) | long (5-7) | v. long (>8 sec)

CONCLUSION:

STYLE:
traditional | in-between | modern

rating: ☆ ☆ ☆ ☆ ☆

FOOD: **FOOD PAIRING:**

MATCH: perfect | good | neutral | bad

tasting date: location:

tasting partner(s):

wine name:

producer:

region/appellation:

grape varieties:

vintage: alcohol: price:

COLOR DEPTH:
watery | pale | medium | deep | dark

COLOR HUE:
WHITE: greenish | yellow | straw yellow | gold | amber
RED: purplish | ruby | red | garnet | brick | brown
ROSÉ: pink | salmon | orange | copper

CLARITY:
clear | slight haze | cloudy

AROMA INTENSITY:
low | moderate | aromatic | powerful

DEVELOPMENT:
youthful | some age | aged

AROMAS:

DRY/SWEET:
bone dry | dry | off dry | medium sweet | sweet | very sweet

BODY:
very light | light | medium | medium-full | full-bodied | heavy

ACIDITY:
tart | crisp | fresh | smooth | flabby

TANNINS (IF PRESENT):
LEVEL: low | medium | high   TYPE: soft | round | dry | hard

BALANCE:
good | fair | unbalanced (excess: alcohol - acid - tannin - sugar)

FLAVOR INTENSITY:
low | moderate | flavorful | powerful

FLAVORS:

FINISH:
short (< 3 sec) | medium (4-5) | long (5-7) | v. long (>8 sec)

CONCLUSION:

STYLE:
traditional | in-between | modern

rating: ☆ ☆ ☆ ☆ ☆

FOOD: **FOOD PAIRING:**
              MATCH: perfect | good | neutral | bad

tasting date: location:

tasting partner(s):

wine name:

producer:

region/appellation:

grape varieties:

vintage: alcohol: price:

 COLOR DEPTH:
watery | pale | medium | deep | dark

COLOR HUE:
WHITE: greenish | yellow | straw yellow | gold | amber
RED: purplish | ruby | red | garnet | brick | brown
ROSÉ: pink | salmon | orange | copper

CLARITY:
clear | slight haze | cloudy

AROMA INTENSITY:
low | moderate | aromatic | powerful

DEVELOPMENT:
youthful | some age | aged

AROMAS:

DRY/SWEET:
bone dry | dry | off dry | medium sweet | sweet | very sweet

BODY:
very light | light | medium | medium-full | full-bodied | heavy

ACIDITY:
tart | crisp | fresh | smooth | flabby

TANNINS (IF PRESENT):
LEVEL: low | medium | high   TYPE: soft | round | dry | hard

BALANCE:
good | fair | unbalanced (excess: alcohol - acid - tannin - sugar)

FLAVOR INTENSITY:
low | moderate | flavorful | powerful

FLAVORS:

FINISH:
short (< 3 sec) | medium (4-5) | long (5-7) | v. long (>8 sec)

CONCLUSION:

STYLE:
traditional | in-between | modern

rating: ☆ ☆ ☆ ☆ ☆

FOOD: **FOOD PAIRING:**

MATCH: perfect | good | neutral | bad

tasting date: location:

tasting partner(s):

wine name:

producer:

region/appellation:

grape varieties:

vintage: alcohol: price:

COLOR DEPTH:
watery | pale | medium | deep | dark

COLOR HUE:
WHITE: greenish | yellow | straw yellow | gold | amber
RED: purplish | ruby | red | garnet | brick | brown
ROSÉ: pink | salmon | orange | copper

CLARITY:
clear | slight haze | cloudy

AROMA INTENSITY:
low | moderate | aromatic | powerful

DEVELOPMENT:
youthful | some age | aged

AROMAS:

DRY/SWEET:
bone dry | dry | off dry | medium sweet | sweet | very sweet

BODY:
very light | light | medium | medium-full | full-bodied | heavy

ACIDITY:
tart | crisp | fresh | smooth | flabby

TANNINS (IF PRESENT):
LEVEL: low | medium | high   TYPE: soft | round | dry | hard

BALANCE:
good | fair | unbalanced (excess: alcohol - acid - tannin - sugar)

FLAVOR INTENSITY:
low | moderate | flavorful | powerful

FLAVORS:

FINISH:
short (< 3 sec) | medium (4-5) | long (5-7) | v. long (>8 sec)

CONCLUSION:

STYLE:
traditional | in-between | modern

rating: ☆ ☆ ☆ ☆ ☆

FOOD: **FOOD PAIRING:**
              MATCH: perfect | good | neutral | bad

tasting date: location:

tasting partner(s):

wine name:

producer:

region/appellation:

grape varieties:

vintage: alcohol: price:

COLOR DEPTH:
watery | pale | medium | deep | dark

COLOR HUE:
WHITE: greenish | yellow | straw yellow | gold | amber
RED: purplish | ruby | red | garnet | brick | brown
ROSÉ: pink | salmon | orange | copper

CLARITY:
clear | slight haze | cloudy

AROMA INTENSITY:
low | moderate | aromatic | powerful

DEVELOPMENT:
youthful | some age | aged

AROMAS:

DRY/SWEET:
bone dry | dry | off dry | medium sweet | sweet | very sweet

BODY:
very light | light | medium | medium-full | full-bodied | heavy

ACIDITY:
tart | crisp | fresh | smooth | flabby

TANNINS (IF PRESENT):
LEVEL: low | medium | high   TYPE: soft | round | dry | hard

BALANCE:
good | fair | unbalanced (excess: alcohol - acid - tannin - sugar)

FLAVOR INTENSITY:
low | moderate | flavorful | powerful

FLAVORS:

FINISH:
short (< 3 sec) | medium (4-5) | long (5-7) | v. long (>8 sec)

CONCLUSION:

STYLE:
traditional | in-between | modern

rating: ☆ ☆ ☆ ☆ ☆

FOOD: **FOOD PAIRING:**
                MATCH: perfect | good | neutral | bad

tasting date: location:

tasting partner(s):

wine name:

producer:

region/appellation:

grape varieties:

vintage: alcohol: price:

COLOR DEPTH:
watery | pale | medium | deep | dark

COLOR HUE:
WHITE: greenish | yellow | straw yellow | gold | amber
RED: purplish | ruby | red | garnet | brick | brown
ROSÉ: pink | salmon | orange | copper

CLARITY:
clear | slight haze | cloudy

AROMA INTENSITY:
low | moderate | aromatic | powerful

DEVELOPMENT:
youthful | some age | aged

AROMAS:

DRY/SWEET:
bone dry | dry | off dry | medium sweet | sweet | very sweet

BODY:
very light | light | medium | medium-full | full-bodied | heavy

ACIDITY:
tart | crisp | fresh | smooth | flabby

TANNINS (IF PRESENT):
LEVEL: low | medium | high   TYPE: soft | round | dry | hard

BALANCE:
good | fair | unbalanced (excess: alcohol - acid - tannin - sugar)

FLAVOR INTENSITY:
low | moderate | flavorful | powerful

FLAVORS:

FINISH:
short (< 3 sec) | medium (4-5) | long (5-7) | v. long (>8 sec)

CONCLUSION:

STYLE:
traditional | in-between | modern

rating: ☆ ☆ ☆ ☆ ☆

FOOD: **FOOD PAIRING:**

MATCH: perfect | good | neutral | bad

tasting date: location:

tasting partner(s):

wine name:

producer:

region/appellation:

grape varieties:

vintage: alcohol: price:

COLOR DEPTH:
watery | pale | medium | deep | dark

COLOR HUE:
WHITE: greenish | yellow | straw yellow | gold | amber
RED: purplish | ruby | red | garnet | brick | brown
ROSÉ: pink | salmon | orange | copper

CLARITY:
clear | slight haze | cloudy

AROMA INTENSITY:
low | moderate | aromatic | powerful

DEVELOPMENT:
youthful | some age | aged

AROMAS:

DRY/SWEET:
bone dry | dry | off dry | medium sweet | sweet | very sweet

BODY:
very light | light | medium | medium-full | full-bodied | heavy

ACIDITY:
tart | crisp | fresh | smooth | flabby

TANNINS (IF PRESENT):
LEVEL: low | medium | high   TYPE: soft | round | dry | hard

BALANCE:
good | fair | unbalanced (excess: alcohol - acid - tannin - sugar)

FLAVOR INTENSITY:
low | moderate | flavorful | powerful

FLAVORS:

FINISH:
short (< 3 sec) | medium (4-5) | long (5-7) | v. long (>8 sec)

CONCLUSION:

STYLE:
traditional | in-between | modern

rating: ☆ ☆ ☆ ☆ ☆

FOOD: **FOOD PAIRING:**

MATCH: perfect | good | neutral | bad

tasting date: location:

tasting partner(s):

wine name:

producer:

region/appellation:

grape varieties:

vintage: alcohol: price:

COLOR DEPTH:
watery | pale | medium | deep | dark
COLOR HUE:
WHITE: greenish | yellow | straw yellow | gold | amber
RED: purplish | ruby | red | garnet | brick | brown
ROSÉ: pink | salmon | orange | copper
CLARITY:
clear | slight haze | cloudy

AROMA INTENSITY:
low | moderate | aromatic | powerful
DEVELOPMENT:
youthful | some age | aged
AROMAS:

DRY/SWEET:
bone dry | dry | off dry | medium sweet | sweet | very sweet
BODY:
very light | light | medium | medium-full | full-bodied | heavy
ACIDITY:
tart | crisp | fresh | smooth | flabby
TANNINS (IF PRESENT):
LEVEL: low | medium | high   TYPE: soft | round | dry | hard
BALANCE:
good | fair | unbalanced (excess: alcohol - acid - tannin - sugar)
FLAVOR INTENSITY:
low | moderate | flavorful | powerful
FLAVORS:

FINISH:
short (< 3 sec) | medium (4-5) | long (5-7) | v. long (>8 sec)
CONCLUSION:

STYLE:
traditional | in-between | modern
rating: ☆ ☆ ☆ ☆ ☆

FOOD: **FOOD PAIRING:**
MATCH: perfect | good | neutral | bad

tasting date: location:

tasting partner(s):

wine name:

producer:

region/appellation:

grape varieties:

vintage: alcohol: price:

COLOR DEPTH:
watery | pale | medium | deep | dark

COLOR HUE:
WHITE: greenish | yellow | straw yellow | gold | amber
RED: purplish | ruby | red | garnet | brick | brown
ROSÉ: pink | salmon | orange | copper

CLARITY:
clear | slight haze | cloudy

AROMA INTENSITY:
low | moderate | aromatic | powerful

DEVELOPMENT:
youthful | some age | aged

AROMAS:

DRY/SWEET:
bone dry | dry | off dry | medium sweet | sweet | very sweet

BODY:
very light | light | medium | medium-full | full-bodied | heavy

ACIDITY:
tart | crisp | fresh | smooth | flabby

TANNINS (IF PRESENT):
LEVEL: low | medium | high   TYPE: soft | round | dry | hard

BALANCE:
good | fair | unbalanced (excess: alcohol - acid - tannin - sugar)

FLAVOR INTENSITY:
low | moderate | flavorful | powerful

FLAVORS:

FINISH:
short (< 3 sec) | medium (4-5) | long (5-7) | v. long (>8 sec)

CONCLUSION:

STYLE:
traditional | in-between | modern

rating: ☆ ☆ ☆ ☆ ☆

FOOD: **FOOD PAIRING:**

MATCH: perfect | good | neutral | bad

tasting date: location:

tasting partner(s):

wine name:

producer:

region/appellation:

grape varieties:

vintage: alcohol: price:

COLOR DEPTH:
watery | pale | medium | deep | dark

COLOR HUE:
WHITE: greenish | yellow | straw yellow | gold | amber
RED: purplish | ruby | red | garnet | brick | brown
ROSÉ: pink | salmon | orange | copper

CLARITY:
clear | slight haze | cloudy

AROMA INTENSITY:
low | moderate | aromatic | powerful

DEVELOPMENT:
youthful | some age | aged

AROMAS:

DRY/SWEET:
bone dry | dry | off dry | medium sweet | sweet | very sweet

BODY:
very light | light | medium | medium-full | full-bodied | heavy

ACIDITY:
tart | crisp | fresh | smooth | flabby

TANNINS (IF PRESENT):
LEVEL: low | medium | high   TYPE: soft | round | dry | hard

BALANCE:
good | fair | unbalanced (excess: alcohol - acid - tannin - sugar)

FLAVOR INTENSITY:
low | moderate | flavorful | powerful

FLAVORS:

FINISH:
short (< 3 sec) | medium (4-5) | long (5-7) | v. long (>8 sec)

CONCLUSION:

STYLE:
traditional | in-between | modern

rating: ☆ ☆ ☆ ☆ ☆

FOOD: **FOOD PAIRING:**
                MATCH: perfect | good | neutral | bad

tasting date: location:

tasting partner(s):

wine name:

producer:

region/appellation:

grape varieties:

vintage: alcohol: price:

 COLOR DEPTH:
watery | pale | medium | deep | dark

COLOR HUE:
WHITE: greenish | yellow | straw yellow | gold | amber
RED: purplish | ruby | red | garnet | brick | brown
ROSÉ: pink | salmon | orange | copper

CLARITY:
clear | slight haze | cloudy

 AROMA INTENSITY:
low | moderate | aromatic | powerful

DEVELOPMENT:
youthful | some age | aged

AROMAS:

DRY/SWEET:
bone dry | dry | off dry | medium sweet | sweet | very sweet

BODY:
very light | light | medium | medium-full | full-bodied | heavy

ACIDITY:
tart | crisp | fresh | smooth | flabby

TANNINS (IF PRESENT):
LEVEL: low | medium | high   TYPE: soft | round | dry | hard

BALANCE:
good | fair | unbalanced (excess: alcohol - acid - tannin - sugar)

FLAVOR INTENSITY:
low | moderate | flavorful | powerful

FLAVORS:

FINISH:
short (< 3 sec) | medium (4-5) | long (5-7) | v. long (>8 sec)

CONCLUSION:

STYLE:
traditional | in-between | modern

rating: ☆ ☆ ☆ ☆ ☆

FOOD: **FOOD PAIRING:**
                  MATCH: perfect | good | neutral | bad

tasting date: location:

tasting partner(s):

wine name:

producer:

region/appellation:

grape varieties:

vintage: alcohol: price:

COLOR DEPTH:
watery | pale | medium | deep | dark

COLOR HUE:
WHITE: greenish | yellow | straw yellow | gold | amber
RED: purplish | ruby | red | garnet | brick | brown
ROSÉ: pink | salmon | orange | copper

CLARITY:
clear | slight haze | cloudy

AROMA INTENSITY:
low | moderate | aromatic | powerful

DEVELOPMENT:
youthful | some age | aged

AROMAS:

DRY/SWEET:
bone dry | dry | off dry | medium sweet | sweet | very sweet

BODY:
very light | light | medium | medium-full | full-bodied | heavy

ACIDITY:
tart | crisp | fresh | smooth | flabby

TANNINS (IF PRESENT):
LEVEL: low | medium | high   TYPE: soft | round | dry | hard

BALANCE:
good | fair | unbalanced (excess: alcohol - acid - tannin - sugar)

FLAVOR INTENSITY:
low | moderate | flavorful | powerful

FLAVORS:

FINISH:
short (< 3 sec) | medium (4-5) | long (5-7) | v. long (>8 sec)

CONCLUSION:

STYLE:
traditional | in-between | modern

rating: ☆ ☆ ☆ ☆ ☆

FOOD: ## FOOD PAIRING:
MATCH: perfect | good | neutral | bad

tasting date: location:

tasting partner(s):

wine name:

producer:

region/appellation:

grape varieties:

vintage: alcohol: price:

COLOR DEPTH:
watery | pale | medium | deep | dark

COLOR HUE:
WHITE: greenish | yellow | straw yellow | gold | amber
RED: purplish | ruby | red | garnet | brick | brown
ROSÉ: pink | salmon | orange | copper

CLARITY:
clear | slight haze | cloudy

AROMA INTENSITY:
low | moderate | aromatic | powerful

DEVELOPMENT:
youthful | some age | aged

AROMAS:

DRY/SWEET:
bone dry | dry | off dry | medium sweet | sweet | very sweet

BODY:
very light | light | medium | medium-full | full-bodied | heavy

ACIDITY:
tart | crisp | fresh | smooth | flabby

TANNINS (IF PRESENT):
LEVEL: low | medium | high   TYPE: soft | round | dry | hard

BALANCE:
good | fair | unbalanced (excess: alcohol - acid - tannin - sugar)

FLAVOR INTENSITY:
low | moderate | flavorful | powerful

FLAVORS:

FINISH:
short (< 3 sec) | medium (4-5) | long (5-7) | v. long (>8 sec)

CONCLUSION:

STYLE:
traditional | in-between | modern

rating: ☆ ☆ ☆ ☆ ☆

FOOD: **FOOD PAIRING:**

MATCH: perfect | good | neutral | bad

tasting date: location:

tasting partner(s):

wine name:

producer:

region/appellation:

grape varieties:

vintage: alcohol: price:

COLOR DEPTH:
watery | pale | medium | deep | dark

COLOR HUE:
WHITE: greenish | yellow | straw yellow | gold | amber
RED: purplish | ruby | red | garnet | brick | brown
ROSÉ: pink | salmon | orange | copper

CLARITY:
clear | slight haze | cloudy

AROMA INTENSITY:
low | moderate | aromatic | powerful

DEVELOPMENT:
youthful | some age | aged

AROMAS:

DRY/SWEET:
bone dry | dry | off dry | medium sweet | sweet | very sweet

BODY:
very light | light | medium | medium-full | full-bodied | heavy

ACIDITY:
tart | crisp | fresh | smooth | flabby

TANNINS (IF PRESENT):
LEVEL: low | medium | high   TYPE: soft | round | dry | hard

BALANCE:
good | fair | unbalanced (excess: alcohol - acid - tannin - sugar)

FLAVOR INTENSITY:
low | moderate | flavorful | powerful

FLAVORS:

FINISH:
short (< 3 sec) | medium (4-5) | long (5-7) | v. long (>8 sec)

CONCLUSION:

STYLE:
traditional | in-between | modern

rating: ☆ ☆ ☆ ☆ ☆

FOOD: **FOOD PAIRING:**
                    MATCH: perfect | good | neutral | bad

tasting date: location:

tasting partner(s):

wine name:

producer:

region/appellation:

grape varieties:

vintage: alcohol: price:

COLOR DEPTH:
watery | pale | medium | deep | dark

COLOR HUE:
WHITE: greenish | yellow | straw yellow | gold | amber
RED: purplish | ruby | red | garnet | brick | brown
ROSÉ: pink | salmon | orange | copper

CLARITY:
clear | slight haze | cloudy

AROMA INTENSITY:
low | moderate | aromatic | powerful

DEVELOPMENT:
youthful | some age | aged

AROMAS:

DRY/SWEET:
bone dry | dry | off dry | medium sweet | sweet | very sweet

BODY:
very light | light | medium | medium-full | full-bodied | heavy

ACIDITY:
tart | crisp | fresh | smooth | flabby

TANNINS (IF PRESENT):
LEVEL: low | medium | high   TYPE: soft | round | dry | hard

BALANCE:
good | fair | unbalanced (excess: alcohol - acid - tannin - sugar)

FLAVOR INTENSITY:
low | moderate | flavorful | powerful

FLAVORS:

FINISH:
short (< 3 sec) | medium (4-5) | long (5-7) | v. long (>8 sec)

CONCLUSION:

STYLE:
traditional | in-between | modern

rating: ☆ ☆ ☆ ☆ ☆

FOOD: **FOOD PAIRING:**

MATCH: perfect | good | neutral | bad

tasting date: location:

tasting partner(s):

wine name:

producer:

region/appellation:

grape varieties:

vintage: alcohol: price:

COLOR DEPTH:
watery | pale | medium | deep | dark

COLOR HUE:
WHITE: greenish | yellow | straw yellow | gold | amber
RED: purplish | ruby | red | garnet | brick | brown
ROSÉ: pink | salmon | orange | copper

CLARITY:
clear | slight haze | cloudy

AROMA INTENSITY:
low | moderate | aromatic | powerful

DEVELOPMENT:
youthful | some age | aged

AROMAS:

DRY/SWEET:
bone dry | dry | off dry | medium sweet | sweet | very sweet

BODY:
very light | light | medium | medium-full | full-bodied | heavy

ACIDITY:
tart | crisp | fresh | smooth | flabby

TANNINS (IF PRESENT):
LEVEL: low | medium | high   TYPE: soft | round | dry | hard

BALANCE:
good | fair | unbalanced (excess: alcohol - acid - tannin - sugar)

FLAVOR INTENSITY:
low | moderate | flavorful | powerful

FLAVORS:

FINISH:
short (< 3 sec) | medium (4-5) | long (5-7) | v. long (>8 sec)

CONCLUSION:

STYLE:
traditional | in-between | modern

rating: ☆ ☆ ☆ ☆ ☆

FOOD:

FOOD PAIRING:
MATCH: perfect | good | neutral | bad

tasting date: location:

tasting partner(s):

wine name:

producer:

region/appellation:

grape varieties:

vintage: alcohol: price:

COLOR DEPTH:
watery | pale | medium | deep | dark

COLOR HUE:
WHITE: greenish | yellow | straw yellow | gold | amber
RED: purplish | ruby | red | garnet | brick | brown
ROSÉ: pink | salmon | orange | copper

CLARITY:
clear | slight haze | cloudy

AROMA INTENSITY:
low | moderate | aromatic | powerful

DEVELOPMENT:
youthful | some age | aged

AROMAS:

DRY/SWEET:
bone dry | dry | off dry | medium sweet | sweet | very sweet

BODY:
very light | light | medium | medium-full | full-bodied | heavy

ACIDITY:
tart | crisp | fresh | smooth | flabby

TANNINS (IF PRESENT):
LEVEL: low | medium | high   TYPE: soft | round | dry | hard

BALANCE:
good | fair | unbalanced (excess: alcohol - acid - tannin - sugar)

FLAVOR INTENSITY:
low | moderate | flavorful | powerful

FLAVORS:

FINISH:
short (< 3 sec) | medium (4-5) | long (5-7) | v. long (>8 sec)

CONCLUSION:

STYLE:
traditional | in-between | modern

rating: ☆ ☆ ☆ ☆ ☆

FOOD: **FOOD PAIRING:**

MATCH: perfect | good | neutral | bad

tasting date: location:

tasting partner(s):

wine name:

producer:

region/appellation:

grape varieties:

vintage: alcohol: price:

COLOR DEPTH:
watery | pale | medium | deep | dark

COLOR HUE:
WHITE: greenish | yellow | straw yellow | gold | amber
RED: purplish | ruby | red | garnet | brick | brown
ROSÉ: pink | salmon | orange | copper

CLARITY:
clear | slight haze | cloudy

AROMA INTENSITY:
low | moderate | aromatic | powerful

DEVELOPMENT:
youthful | some age | aged

AROMAS:

DRY/SWEET:
bone dry | dry | off dry | medium sweet | sweet | very sweet

BODY:
very light | light | medium | medium-full | full-bodied | heavy

ACIDITY:
tart | crisp | fresh | smooth | flabby

TANNINS (IF PRESENT):
LEVEL: low | medium | high   TYPE: soft | round | dry | hard

BALANCE:
good | fair | unbalanced (excess: alcohol - acid - tannin - sugar)

FLAVOR INTENSITY:
low | moderate | flavorful | powerful

FLAVORS:

FINISH:
short (< 3 sec) | medium (4-5) | long (5-7) | v. long (>8 sec)

CONCLUSION:

STYLE:
traditional | in-between | modern

rating: ☆ ☆ ☆ ☆ ☆

FOOD: ## FOOD PAIRING:
MATCH: perfect | good | neutral | bad

tasting date: location:

tasting partner(s):

wine name:

producer:

region/appellation:

grape varieties:

vintage: alcohol: price:

COLOR DEPTH:
watery | pale | medium | deep | dark

COLOR HUE:
WHITE: greenish | yellow | straw yellow | gold | amber
RED: purplish | ruby | red | garnet | brick | brown
ROSÉ: pink | salmon | orange | copper

CLARITY:
clear | slight haze | cloudy

AROMA INTENSITY:
low | moderate | aromatic | powerful

DEVELOPMENT:
youthful | some age | aged

AROMAS:

DRY/SWEET:
bone dry | dry | off dry | medium sweet | sweet | very sweet

BODY:
very light | light | medium | medium-full | full-bodied | heavy

ACIDITY:
tart | crisp | fresh | smooth | flabby

TANNINS (IF PRESENT):
LEVEL: low | medium | high   TYPE: soft | round | dry | hard

BALANCE:
good | fair | unbalanced (excess: alcohol - acid - tannin - sugar)

FLAVOR INTENSITY:
low | moderate | flavorful | powerful

FLAVORS:

FINISH:
short (< 3 sec) | medium (4-5) | long (5-7) | v. long (>8 sec)

CONCLUSION:

STYLE:
traditional | in-between | modern

rating: ☆ ☆ ☆ ☆ ☆

FOOD: **FOOD PAIRING:**

MATCH: perfect | good | neutral | bad

tasting date: location:

tasting partner(s):

wine name:

producer:

region/appellation:

grape varieties:

vintage: alcohol: price:

COLOR DEPTH:
watery | pale | medium | deep | dark

COLOR HUE:
WHITE: greenish | yellow | straw yellow | gold | amber
RED: purplish | ruby | red | garnet | brick | brown
ROSÉ: pink | salmon | orange | copper

CLARITY:
clear | slight haze | cloudy

AROMA INTENSITY:
low | moderate | aromatic | powerful

DEVELOPMENT:
youthful | some age | aged

AROMAS:

DRY/SWEET:
bone dry | dry | off dry | medium sweet | sweet | very sweet

BODY:
very light | light | medium | medium-full | full-bodied | heavy

ACIDITY:
tart | crisp | fresh | smooth | flabby

TANNINS (IF PRESENT):
LEVEL: low | medium | high   TYPE: soft | round | dry | hard

BALANCE:
good | fair | unbalanced (excess: alcohol - acid - tannin - sugar)

FLAVOR INTENSITY:
low | moderate | flavorful | powerful

FLAVORS:

FINISH:
short (< 3 sec) | medium (4-5) | long (5-7) | v. long (>8 sec)

CONCLUSION:

STYLE:
traditional | in-between | modern

rating: ☆ ☆ ☆ ☆ ☆

FOOD: ### FOOD PAIRING:

MATCH: perfect | good | neutral | bad

tasting date: location:

tasting partner(s):

wine name:

producer:

region/appellation:

grape varieties:

vintage: alcohol: price:

COLOR DEPTH:
watery | pale | medium | deep | dark

COLOR HUE:
WHITE: greenish | yellow | straw yellow | gold | amber
RED: purplish | ruby | red | garnet | brick | brown
ROSÉ: pink | salmon | orange | copper

CLARITY:
clear | slight haze | cloudy

AROMA INTENSITY:
löw | moderate | aromatic | powerful

DEVELOPMENT:
youthful | some age | aged

AROMAS:

DRY/SWEET:
bone dry | dry | off dry | medium sweet | sweet | very sweet

BODY:
very light | light | medium | medium-full | full-bodied | heavy

ACIDITY:
tart | crisp | fresh | smooth | flabby

TANNINS (IF PRESENT):
LEVEL: low | medium | high   TYPE: soft | round | dry | hard

BALANCE:
good | fair | unbalanced (excess: alcohol - acid - tannin - sugar)

FLAVOR INTENSITY:
low | moderate | flavorful | powerful

FLAVORS:

FINISH:
short (< 3 sec) | medium (4-5) | long (5-7) | v. long (>8 sec)

CONCLUSION:

STYLE:
traditional | in-between | modern

rating: ☆ ☆ ☆ ☆ ☆

FOOD: **FOOD PAIRING:**

MATCH: perfect | good | neutral | bad

tasting date: location:

tasting partner(s):

wine name:

producer:

region/appellation:

grape varieties:

vintage: alcohol: price:

COLOR DEPTH:
watery | pale | medium | deep | dark

COLOR HUE:
WHITE: greenish | yellow | straw yellow | gold | amber
RED: purplish | ruby | red | garnet | brick | brown
ROSÉ: pink | salmon | orange | copper

CLARITY:
clear | slight haze | cloudy

AROMA INTENSITY:
low | moderate | aromatic | powerful

DEVELOPMENT:
youthful | some age | aged

AROMAS:

DRY/SWEET:
bone dry | dry | off dry | medium sweet | sweet | very sweet

BODY:
very light | light | medium | medium-full | full-bodied | heavy

ACIDITY:
tart | crisp | fresh | smooth | flabby

TANNINS (IF PRESENT):
LEVEL: low | medium | high   TYPE: soft | round | dry | hard

BALANCE:
good | fair | unbalanced (excess: alcohol - acid - tannin - sugar)

FLAVOR INTENSITY:
low | moderate | flavorful | powerful

FLAVORS:

FINISH:
short (< 3 sec) | medium (4-5) | long (5-7) | v. long (>8 sec)

CONCLUSION:

STYLE:
traditional | in-between | modern

rating: ☆ ☆ ☆ ☆ ☆

FOOD: ### FOOD PAIRING:
MATCH: perfect | good | neutral | bad

tasting date: location:

tasting partner(s):

wine name:

producer:

region/appellation:

grape varieties:

vintage: alcohol: price:

 COLOR DEPTH:
watery | pale | medium | deep | dark

COLOR HUE:
WHITE: greenish | yellow | straw yellow | gold | amber
RED: purplish | ruby | red | garnet | brick | brown
ROSÉ: pink | salmon | orange | copper

CLARITY:
clear | slight haze | cloudy

 AROMA INTENSITY:
low | moderate | aromatic | powerful

DEVELOPMENT:
youthful | some age | aged

AROMAS:

 DRY/SWEET:
bone dry | dry | off dry | medium sweet | sweet | very sweet

BODY:
very light | light | medium | medium-full | full-bodied | heavy

ACIDITY:
tart | crisp | fresh | smooth | flabby

TANNINS (IF PRESENT):
LEVEL: low | medium | high   TYPE: soft | round | dry | hard

BALANCE:
good | fair | unbalanced (excess: alcohol - acid - tannin - sugar)

FLAVOR INTENSITY:
low | moderate | flavorful | powerful

FLAVORS:

FINISH:
short (< 3 sec) | medium (4-5) | long (5-7) | v. long (>8 sec)

CONCLUSION:

STYLE:
traditional | in-between | modern

rating: ☆ ☆ ☆ ☆ ☆

FOOD: **FOOD PAIRING:**
              MATCH: perfect | good | neutral | bad

tasting date: location:

tasting partner(s):

wine name:

producer:

region/appellation:

grape varieties:

vintage: alcohol: price:

COLOR DEPTH:
watery | pale | medium | deep | dark

COLOR HUE:
WHITE: greenish | yellow | straw yellow | gold | amber
RED: purplish | ruby | red | garnet | brick | brown
ROSÉ: pink | salmon | orange | copper

CLARITY:
clear | slight haze | cloudy

AROMA INTENSITY:
low | moderate | aromatic | powerful

DEVELOPMENT:
youthful | some age | aged

AROMAS:

DRY/SWEET:
bone dry | dry | off dry | medium sweet | sweet | very sweet

BODY:
very light | light | medium | medium-full | full-bodied | heavy

ACIDITY:
tart | crisp | fresh | smooth | flabby

TANNINS (IF PRESENT):
LEVEL: low | medium | high   TYPE: soft | round | dry | hard

BALANCE:
good | fair | unbalanced (excess: alcohol - acid - tannin - sugar)

FLAVOR INTENSITY:
low | moderate | flavorful | powerful

FLAVORS:

FINISH:
short (< 3 sec) | medium (4-5) | long (5-7) | v. long (>8 sec)

CONCLUSION:

STYLE:
traditional | in-between | modern

rating: ☆ ☆ ☆ ☆ ☆

FOOD: ## FOOD PAIRING:
MATCH: perfect | good | neutral | bad

tasting date: location:

tasting partner(s):

wine name:

producer:

region/appellation:

grape varieties:

vintage: alcohol: price:

 ### COLOR DEPTH:
watery | pale | medium | deep | dark

COLOR HUE:
WHITE: greenish | yellow | straw yellow | gold | amber
RED: purplish | ruby | red | garnet | brick | brown
ROSÉ: pink | salmon | orange | copper

CLARITY:
clear | slight haze | cloudy

 ### AROMA INTENSITY:
low | moderate | aromatic | powerful

DEVELOPMENT:
youthful | some age | aged

AROMAS:

 ### DRY/SWEET:
bone dry | dry | off dry | medium sweet | sweet | very sweet

BODY:
very light | light | medium | medium-full | full-bodied | heavy

ACIDITY:
tart | crisp | fresh | smooth | flabby

TANNINS (IF PRESENT):
LEVEL: low | medium | high   TYPE: soft | round | dry | hard

BALANCE:
good | fair | unbalanced (excess: alcohol - acid - tannin - sugar)

FLAVOR INTENSITY:
low | moderate | flavorful | powerful

FLAVORS:

FINISH:
short (< 3 sec) | medium (4-5) | long (5-7) | v. long (>8 sec)

CONCLUSION:

STYLE:
traditional | in-between | modern

rating: ☆ ☆ ☆ ☆ ☆

FOOD: ### FOOD PAIRING:
MATCH: perfect | good | neutral | bad

tasting date: location:

tasting partner(s):

wine name:

producer:

region/appellation:

grape varieties:

vintage: alcohol: price:

COLOR DEPTH:
watery | pale | medium | deep | dark

COLOR HUE:
WHITE: greenish | yellow | straw yellow | gold | amber
RED: purplish | ruby | red | garnet | brick | brown
ROSÉ: pink | salmon | orange | copper

CLARITY:
clear | slight haze | cloudy

AROMA INTENSITY:
low | moderate | aromatic | powerful

DEVELOPMENT:
youthful | some age | aged

AROMAS:

.

DRY/SWEET:
bone dry | dry | off dry | medium sweet | sweet | very sweet

BODY:
very light | light | medium | medium-full | full-bodied | heavy

ACIDITY:
tart | crisp | fresh | smooth | flabby

TANNINS (IF PRESENT):
LEVEL: low | medium | high   TYPE: soft | round | dry | hard

BALANCE:
good | fair | unbalanced (excess: alcohol - acid - tannin - sugar)

FLAVOR INTENSITY:
low | moderate | flavorful | powerful

FLAVORS:

FINISH:
short (< 3 sec) | medium (4-5) | long (5-7) | v. long (>8 sec)

CONCLUSION:

STYLE:
traditional | in-between | modern

rating: ☆ ☆ ☆ ☆ ☆

FOOD: **FOOD PAIRING:**
                MATCH: perfect | good | neutral | bad

tasting date: location:

tasting partner(s):

wine name:

producer:

region/appellation:

grape varieties:

vintage: alcohol: price:

COLOR DEPTH:
watery | pale | medium | deep | dark

COLOR HUE:
WHITE: greenish | yellow | straw yellow | gold | amber
RED: purplish | ruby | red | garnet | brick | brown
ROSÉ: pink | salmon | orange | copper

CLARITY:
clear | slight haze | cloudy

AROMA INTENSITY:
low | moderate | aromatic | powerful

DEVELOPMENT:
youthful | some age | aged

AROMAS:

DRY/SWEET:
bone dry | dry | off dry | medium sweet | sweet | very sweet

BODY:
very light | light | medium | medium-full | full-bodied | heavy

ACIDITY:
tart | crisp | fresh | smooth | flabby

TANNINS (IF PRESENT):
LEVEL: low | medium | high   TYPE: soft | round | dry | hard

BALANCE:
good | fair | unbalanced (excess: alcohol - acid - tannin - sugar)

FLAVOR INTENSITY:
low | moderate | flavorful | powerful

FLAVORS:

FINISH:
short (< 3 sec) | medium (4-5) | long (5-7) | v. long (>8 sec)

CONCLUSION:

STYLE:
traditional | in-between | modern

rating: ☆ ☆ ☆ ☆ ☆

FOOD: **FOOD PAIRING:**

MATCH: perfect | good | neutral | bad

tasting date: location:

tasting partner(s):

wine name:

producer:

region/appellation:

grape varieties:

vintage: alcohol: price:

COLOR DEPTH:
watery | pale | medium | deep | dark

COLOR HUE:
WHITE: greenish | yellow | straw yellow | gold | amber
RED: purplish | ruby | red | garnet | brick | brown
ROSÉ: pink | salmon | orange | copper

CLARITY:
clear | slight haze | cloudy

AROMA INTENSITY:
low | moderate | aromatic | powerful

DEVELOPMENT:
youthful | some age | aged

AROMAS:

DRY/SWEET:
bone dry | dry | off dry | medium sweet | sweet | very sweet

BODY:
very light | light | medium | medium-full | full-bodied | heavy

ACIDITY:
tart | crisp | fresh | smooth | flabby

TANNINS (IF PRESENT):
LEVEL: low | medium | high   TYPE: soft | round | dry | hard

BALANCE:
good | fair | unbalanced (excess: alcohol - acid - tannin - sugar)

FLAVOR INTENSITY:
low | moderate | flavorful | powerful

FLAVORS:

FINISH:
short (< 3 sec) | medium (4-5) | long (5-7) | v. long (>8 sec)

CONCLUSION:

STYLE:
traditional | in-between | modern

rating: ☆ ☆ ☆ ☆ ☆

FOOD:
FOOD PAIRING:
MATCH: perfect | good | neutral | bad

tasting date: location:

tasting partner(s):

wine name:

producer:

region/appellation:

grape varieties:

vintage: alcohol: price:

COLOR DEPTH:
watery | pale | medium | deep | dark

COLOR HUE:
WHITE: greenish | yellow | straw yellow | gold | amber
RED: purplish | ruby | red | garnet | brick | brown
ROSÉ: pink | salmon | orange | copper

CLARITY:
clear | slight haze | cloudy

AROMA INTENSITY:
low | moderate | aromatic | powerful

DEVELOPMENT:
youthful | some age | aged

AROMAS:

DRY/SWEET:
bone dry | dry | off dry | medium sweet | sweet | very sweet

BODY:
very light | light | medium | medium-full | full-bodied | heavy

ACIDITY:
tart | crisp | fresh | smooth | flabby

TANNINS (IF PRESENT):
LEVEL: low | medium | high   TYPE: soft | round | dry | hard

BALANCE:
good | fair | unbalanced (excess: alcohol - acid - tannin - sugar)

FLAVOR INTENSITY:
low | moderate | flavorful | powerful

FLAVORS:

FINISH:
short (< 3 sec) | medium (4-5) | long (5-7) | v. long (>8 sec)

CONCLUSION:

STYLE:
traditional | in-between | modern

rating: ☆ ☆ ☆ ☆ ☆

FOOD: **FOOD PAIRING:**
                    MATCH: perfect | good | neutral | bad

tasting date: location:

tasting partner(s):

wine name:

producer:

region/appellation:

grape varieties:

vintage: alcohol: price:

COLOR DEPTH:
watery | pale | medium | deep | dark

COLOR HUE:
WHITE: greenish | yellow | straw yellow | gold | amber
RED: purplish | ruby | red | garnet | brick | brown
ROSÉ: pink | salmon | orange | copper

CLARITY:
clear | slight haze | cloudy

AROMA INTENSITY:
low | moderate | aromatic | powerful

DEVELOPMENT:
youthful | some age | aged

AROMAS:

DRY/SWEET:
bone dry | dry | off dry | medium sweet | sweet | very sweet

BODY:
very light | light | medium | medium-full | full-bodied | heavy

ACIDITY:
tart | crisp | fresh | smooth | flabby

TANNINS (IF PRESENT):
LEVEL: low | medium | high   TYPE: soft | round | dry | hard

BALANCE:
good | fair | unbalanced (excess: alcohol - acid - tannin - sugar)

FLAVOR INTENSITY:
low | moderate | flavorful | powerful

FLAVORS:

FINISH:
short (< 3 sec) | medium (4-5) | long (5-7) | v. long (>8 sec)

CONCLUSION:

STYLE:
traditional | in-between | modern

rating: ☆ ☆ ☆ ☆ ☆

FOOD: **FOOD PAIRING:**
                MATCH: perfect | good | neutral | bad

tasting date: location:

tasting partner(s):

wine name:

producer:

region/appellation:

grape varieties:

vintage: alcohol: price:

COLOR DEPTH:
watery | pale | medium | deep | dark

COLOR HUE:
WHITE: greenish | yellow | straw yellow | gold | amber
RED: purplish | ruby | red | garnet | brick | brown
ROSÉ: pink | salmon | orange | copper

CLARITY:
clear | slight haze | cloudy

AROMA INTENSITY:
low | moderate | aromatic | powerful

DEVELOPMENT:
youthful | some age | aged

AROMAS:

DRY/SWEET:
bone dry | dry | off dry | medium sweet | sweet | very sweet

BODY:
very light | light | medium | medium-full | full-bodied | heavy

ACIDITY:
tart | crisp | fresh | smooth | flabby

TANNINS (IF PRESENT):
LEVEL: low | medium | high   TYPE: soft | round | dry | hard

BALANCE:
good | fair | unbalanced (excess: alcohol - acid - tannin - sugar)

FLAVOR INTENSITY:
low | moderate | flavorful | powerful

FLAVORS:

FINISH:
short (< 3 sec) | medium (4-5) | long (5-7) | v. long (>8 sec)

CONCLUSION:

STYLE:
traditional | in-between | modern

rating: ☆ ☆ ☆ ☆ ☆

FOOD: **FOOD PAIRING:**

MATCH: perfect | good | neutral | bad

tasting date: location:

tasting partner(s):

wine name:

producer:

region/appellation:

grape varieties:

vintage: alcohol: price:

COLOR DEPTH:
watery | pale | medium | deep | dark

COLOR HUE:
WHITE: greenish | yellow | straw yellow | gold | amber
RED: purplish | ruby | red | garnet | brick | brown
ROSÉ: pink | salmon | orange | copper

CLARITY:
clear | slight haze | cloudy

AROMA INTENSITY:
low | moderate | aromatic | powerful

DEVELOPMENT:
youthful | some age | aged

AROMAS:

DRY/SWEET:
bone dry | dry | off dry | medium sweet | sweet | very sweet

BODY:
very light | light | medium | medium-full | full-bodied | heavy

ACIDITY:
tart | crisp | fresh | smooth | flabby

TANNINS (IF PRESENT):
LEVEL: low | medium | high TYPE: soft | round | dry | hard

BALANCE:
good | fair | unbalanced (excess: alcohol - acid - tannin - sugar)

FLAVOR INTENSITY:
low | moderate | flavorful | powerful

FLAVORS:

FINISH:
short (< 3 sec) | medium (4-5) | long (5-7) | v. long (>8 sec)

CONCLUSION:

STYLE:
traditional | in-between | modern

rating: ☆ ☆ ☆ ☆ ☆

FOOD: **FOOD PAIRING:**

MATCH: perfect | good | neutral | bad

tasting date: location:

tasting partner(s):

wine name:

producer:

region/appellation:

grape varieties:

vintage: alcohol: price:

COLOR DEPTH:
watery | pale | medium | deep | dark

COLOR HUE:
WHITE: greenish | yellow | straw yellow | gold | amber
RED: purplish | ruby | red | garnet | brick | brown
ROSÉ: pink | salmon | orange | copper

CLARITY:
clear | slight haze | cloudy

AROMA INTENSITY:
low | moderate | aromatic | powerful

DEVELOPMENT:
youthful | some age | aged

AROMAS:

DRY/SWEET:
bone dry | dry | off dry | medium sweet | sweet | very sweet

BODY:
very light | light | medium | medium-full | full-bodied | heavy

ACIDITY:
tart | crisp | fresh | smooth | flabby

TANNINS (IF PRESENT):
LEVEL: low | medium | high   TYPE: soft | round | dry | hard

BALANCE:
good | fair | unbalanced (excess: alcohol - acid - tannin - sugar)

FLAVOR INTENSITY:
low | moderate | flavorful | powerful

FLAVORS:

FINISH:
short (< 3 sec) | medium (4-5) | long (5-7) | v. long (>8 sec)

CONCLUSION:

STYLE:
traditional | in-between | modern

rating: ☆ ☆ ☆ ☆ ☆

FOOD: **FOOD PAIRING:**

MATCH: perfect | good | neutral | bad

tasting date: location:

tasting partner(s):

wine name:

producer:

region/appellation:

grape varieties:

vintage: alcohol: price:

COLOR DEPTH:
watery | pale | medium | deep | dark

COLOR HUE:
WHITE: greenish | yellow | straw yellow | gold | amber
RED: purplish | ruby | red | garnet | brick | brown
ROSÉ: pink | salmon | orange | copper

CLARITY:
clear | slight haze | cloudy

AROMA INTENSITY:
low | moderate | aromatic | powerful

DEVELOPMENT:
youthful | some age | aged

AROMAS:

DRY/SWEET:
bone dry | dry | off dry | medium sweet | sweet | very sweet

BODY:
very light | light | medium | medium-full | full-bodied | heavy

ACIDITY:
tart | crisp | fresh | smooth | flabby

TANNINS (IF PRESENT):
LEVEL: low | medium | high   TYPE: soft | round | dry | hard

BALANCE:
good | fair | unbalanced (excess: alcohol - acid - tannin - sugar)

FLAVOR INTENSITY:
low | moderate | flavorful | powerful

FLAVORS:

FINISH:
short (< 3 sec) | medium (4-5) | long (5-7) | v. long (>8 sec)

CONCLUSION:

STYLE:
traditional | in-between | modern

rating: ☆ ☆ ☆ ☆ ☆

FOOD: **FOOD PAIRING:**
                    MATCH: perfect | good | neutral | bad

tasting date: location:

tasting partner(s):

wine name:

producer:

region/appellation:

grape varieties:

vintage: alcohol: price:

COLOR DEPTH:
watery | pale | medium | deep | dark

COLOR HUE:
WHITE: greenish | yellow | straw yellow | gold | amber
RED: purplish | ruby | red | garnet | brick | brown
ROSÉ: pink | salmon | orange | copper

CLARITY:
clear | slight haze | cloudy

AROMA INTENSITY:
low | moderate | aromatic | powerful

DEVELOPMENT:
youthful | some age | aged

AROMAS:

DRY/SWEET:
bone dry | dry | off dry | medium sweet | sweet | very sweet

BODY:
very light | light | medium | medium-full | full-bodied | heavy

ACIDITY:
tart | crisp | fresh | smooth | flabby

TANNINS (IF PRESENT):
LEVEL: low | medium | high   TYPE: soft | round | dry | hard

BALANCE:
good | fair | unbalanced (excess: alcohol - acid - tannin - sugar)

FLAVOR INTENSITY:
low | moderate | flavorful | powerful

FLAVORS:

FINISH:
short (< 3 sec) | medium (4-5) | long (5-7) | v. long (>8 sec)

CONCLUSION:

STYLE:
traditional | in-between | modern

rating: ☆ ☆ ☆ ☆ ☆

FOOD: **FOOD PAIRING:**

MATCH: perfect | good | neutral | bad

tasting date: location:

tasting partner(s):

wine name:

producer:

region/appellation:

grape varieties:

vintage: alcohol: price:

COLOR DEPTH:
watery | pale | medium | deep | dark

COLOR HUE:
WHITE: greenish | yellow | straw yellow | gold | amber
RED: purplish | ruby | red | garnet | brick | brown
ROSÉ: pink | salmon | orange | copper

CLARITY:
clear | slight haze | cloudy

AROMA INTENSITY:
low | moderate | aromatic | powerful

DEVELOPMENT:
youthful | some age | aged

AROMAS:

DRY/SWEET:
bone dry | dry | off dry | medium sweet | sweet | very sweet

BODY:
very light | light | medium | medium-full | full-bodied | heavy

ACIDITY:
tart | crisp | fresh | smooth | flabby

TANNINS (IF PRESENT):
LEVEL: low | medium | high   TYPE: soft | round | dry | hard

BALANCE:
good | fair | unbalanced (excess: alcohol - acid - tannin - sugar)

FLAVOR INTENSITY:
low | moderate | flavorful | powerful

FLAVORS:

FINISH:
short (< 3 sec) | medium (4-5) | long (5-7) | v. long (>8 sec)

CONCLUSION:

STYLE:
traditional | in-between | modern

rating: ☆ ☆ ☆ ☆ ☆

FOOD: **FOOD PAIRING:**
                 MATCH: perfect | good | neutral | bad

tasting date: location:

tasting partner(s):

wine name:

producer:

region/appellation:

grape varieties:

vintage: alcohol: price:

COLOR DEPTH:
watery | pale | medium | deep | dark
COLOR HUE:
WHITE: greenish | yellow | straw yellow | gold | amber
RED: purplish | ruby | red | garnet | brick | brown
ROSÉ: pink | salmon | orange | copper
CLARITY:
clear | slight haze | cloudy

AROMA INTENSITY:
low | moderate | aromatic | powerful
DEVELOPMENT:
youthful | some age | aged
AROMAS:

DRY/SWEET:
bone dry | dry | off dry | medium sweet | sweet | very sweet
BODY:
very light | light | medium | medium-full | full-bodied | heavy
ACIDITY:
tart | crisp | fresh | smooth | flabby
TANNINS (IF PRESENT):
LEVEL: low | medium | high   TYPE: soft | round | dry | hard
BALANCE:
good | fair | unbalanced (excess: alcohol - acid - tannin - sugar)
FLAVOR INTENSITY:
low | moderate | flavorful | powerful
FLAVORS:

FINISH:
short (< 3 sec) | medium (4-5) | long (5-7) | v. long (>8 sec)
CONCLUSION:

STYLE:
traditional | in-between | modern
rating: ☆ ☆ ☆ ☆ ☆

FOOD: **FOOD PAIRING:**
                  MATCH: perfect | good | neutral | bad

tasting date: location:

tasting partner(s):

wine name:

producer:

region/appellation:

grape varieties:

vintage: alcohol: price:

COLOR DEPTH:
watery | pale | medium | deep | dark

COLOR HUE:
WHITE: greenish | yellow | straw yellow | gold | amber
RED: purplish | ruby | red | garnet | brick | brown
ROSÉ: pink | salmon | orange | copper

CLARITY:
clear | slight haze | cloudy

AROMA INTENSITY:
low | moderate | aromatic | powerful

DEVELOPMENT:
youthful | some age | aged

AROMAS:

DRY/SWEET:
bone dry | dry | off dry | medium sweet | sweet | very sweet

BODY:
very light | light | medium | medium-full | full-bodied | heavy

ACIDITY:
tart | crisp | fresh | smooth | flabby

TANNINS (IF PRESENT):
LEVEL: low | medium | high   TYPE: soft | round | dry | hard

BALANCE:
good | fair | unbalanced (excess: alcohol - acid - tannin - sugar)

FLAVOR INTENSITY:
low | moderate | flavorful | powerful

FLAVORS:

FINISH:
short (< 3 sec) | medium (4-5) | long (5-7) | v. long (>8 sec)

CONCLUSION:

STYLE:
traditional | in-between | modern

rating: ☆ ☆ ☆ ☆ ☆

FOOD: **FOOD PAIRING:**
                MATCH: perfect | good | neutral | bad

tasting date: location:

tasting partner(s):

wine name:

producer:

region/appellation:

grape varieties:

vintage: alcohol: price:

COLOR DEPTH:
watery | pale | medium | deep | dark

COLOR HUE:
WHITE: greenish | yellow | straw yellow | gold | amber
RED: purplish | ruby | red | garnet | brick | brown
ROSÉ: pink | salmon | orange | copper

CLARITY:
clear | slight haze | cloudy

AROMA INTENSITY:
low | moderate | aromatic | powerful

DEVELOPMENT:
youthful | some age | aged

AROMAS:

DRY/SWEET:
bone dry | dry | off dry | medium sweet | sweet | very sweet

BODY:
very light | light | medium | medium-full | full-bodied | heavy

ACIDITY:
tart | crisp | fresh | smooth | flabby

TANNINS (IF PRESENT):
LEVEL: low | medium | high   TYPE: soft | round | dry | hard

BALANCE:
good | fair | unbalanced (excess: alcohol - acid - tannin - sugar)

FLAVOR INTENSITY:
low | moderate | flavorful | powerful

FLAVORS:

FINISH:
short (< 3 sec) | medium (4-5) | long (5-7) | v. long (>8 sec)

CONCLUSION:

STYLE:
traditional | in-between | modern

rating: ☆ ☆ ☆ ☆ ☆

FOOD: **FOOD PAIRING:**
                 MATCH: perfect | good | neutral | bad

tasting date: location:

tasting partner(s):

wine name:

producer:

region/appellation:

grape varieties:

vintage: alcohol: price:

COLOR DEPTH:
watery | pale | medium | deep | dark

COLOR HUE:
WHITE: greenish | yellow | straw yellow | gold | amber
RED: purplish | ruby | red | garnet | brick | brown
ROSÉ: pink | salmon | orange | copper

CLARITY:
clear | slight haze | cloudy

AROMA INTENSITY:
low | moderate | aromatic | powerful

DEVELOPMENT:
youthful | some age | aged

AROMAS:

DRY/SWEET:
bone dry | dry | off dry | medium sweet | sweet | very sweet

BODY:
very light | light | medium | medium-full | full-bodied | heavy

ACIDITY:
tart | crisp | fresh | smooth | flabby

TANNINS (IF PRESENT):
LEVEL: low | medium | high   TYPE: soft | round | dry | hard

BALANCE:
good | fair | unbalanced (excess: alcohol - acid - tannin - sugar)

FLAVOR INTENSITY:
low | moderate | flavorful | powerful

FLAVORS:

FINISH:
short (< 3 sec) | medium (4-5) | long (5-7) | v. long (>8 sec)

CONCLUSION:

STYLE:
traditional | in-between | modern

rating: ☆ ☆ ☆ ☆ ☆

FOOD: ## FOOD PAIRING:
                    MATCH: perfect | good | neutral | bad

tasting date: location:

tasting partner(s):

wine name:

producer:

region/appellation:

grape varieties:

vintage: alcohol: price:

COLOR DEPTH:
watery | pale | medium | deep | dark

COLOR HUE:
WHITE: greenish | yellow | straw yellow | gold | amber
RED: purplish | ruby | red | garnet | brick | brown
ROSÉ: pink | salmon | orange | copper

CLARITY:
clear | slight haze | cloudy

AROMA INTENSITY:
low | moderate | aromatic | powerful

DEVELOPMENT:
youthful | some age | aged

AROMAS:

DRY/SWEET:
bone dry | dry | off dry | medium sweet | sweet | very sweet

BODY:
very light | light | medium | medium-full | full-bodied | heavy

ACIDITY:
tart | crisp | fresh | smooth | flabby

TANNINS (IF PRESENT):
LEVEL: low | medium | high   TYPE: soft | round | dry | hard

BALANCE:
good | fair | unbalanced (excess: alcohol - acid - tannin - sugar)

FLAVOR INTENSITY:
low | moderate | flavorful | powerful

FLAVORS:

FINISH:
short (< 3 sec) | medium (4-5) | long (5-7) | v. long (>8 sec)

CONCLUSION:

STYLE:
traditional | in-between | modern

rating: ☆ ☆ ☆ ☆ ☆

FOOD: **FOOD PAIRING:**

MATCH: perfect | good | neutral | bad

tasting date: location:

tasting partner(s):

wine name:

producer:

region/appellation:

grape varieties:

vintage: alcohol: price:

COLOR DEPTH:
watery | pale | medium | deep | dark
COLOR HUE:
WHITE: greenish | yellow | straw yellow | gold | amber
RED: purplish | ruby | red | garnet | brick | brown
ROSÉ: pink | salmon | orange | copper

CLARITY:
clear | slight haze | cloudy

AROMA INTENSITY:
low | moderate | aromatic | powerful
DEVELOPMENT:
youthful | some age | aged
AROMAS:

DRY/SWEET:
bone dry | dry | off dry | medium sweet | sweet | very sweet
BODY:
very light | light | medium | medium-full | full-bodied | heavy
ACIDITY:
tart | crisp | fresh | smooth | flabby
TANNINS (IF PRESENT):
LEVEL: low | medium | high   TYPE: soft | round | dry | hard
BALANCE:
good | fair | unbalanced (excess: alcohol - acid - tannin - sugar)
FLAVOR INTENSITY:
low | moderate | flavorful | powerful
FLAVORS:

FINISH:
short (< 3 sec) | medium (4-5) | long (5-7) | v. long (>8 sec)

CONCLUSION:

STYLE:
traditional | in-between | modern

rating: ☆ ☆ ☆ ☆ ☆

FOOD: **FOOD PAIRING:**

MATCH: perfect | good | neutral | bad

tasting date: location:

tasting partner(s):

wine name:

producer:

region/appellation:

grape varieties:

vintage: alcohol: price:

COLOR DEPTH:
watery | pale | medium | deep | dark

COLOR HUE:
WHITE: greenish | yellow | straw yellow | gold | amber
RED: purplish | ruby | red | garnet | brick | brown
ROSÉ: pink | salmon | orange | copper

CLARITY:
clear | slight haze | cloudy

AROMA INTENSITY:
low | moderate | aromatic | powerful

DEVELOPMENT:
youthful | some age | aged

AROMAS:

DRY/SWEET:
bone dry | dry | off dry | medium sweet | sweet | very sweet

BODY:
very light | light | medium | medium-full | full-bodied | heavy

ACIDITY:
tart | crisp | fresh | smooth | flabby

TANNINS (IF PRESENT):
LEVEL: low | medium | high   TYPE: soft | round | dry | hard

BALANCE:
good | fair | unbalanced (excess: alcohol - acid - tannin - sugar)

FLAVOR INTENSITY:
low | moderate | flavorful | powerful

FLAVORS:

FINISH:
short (< 3 sec) | medium (4-5) | long (5-7) | v. long (>8 sec)

CONCLUSION:

STYLE:
traditional | in-between | modern

rating: ☆ ☆ ☆ ☆ ☆

FOOD: **FOOD PAIRING:**

MATCH: perfect | good | neutral | bad

tasting date: location:

tasting partner(s):

wine name:

producer:

region/appellation:

grape varieties:

vintage: alcohol: price:

COLOR DEPTH:
watery | pale | medium | deep | dark

COLOR HUE:
WHITE: greenish | yellow | straw yellow | gold | amber
RED: purplish | ruby | red | garnet | brick | brown
ROSÉ: pink | salmon | orange | copper

CLARITY:
clear | slight haze | cloudy

AROMA INTENSITY:
low | moderate | aromatic | powerful

DEVELOPMENT:
youthful | some age | aged

AROMAS:

DRY/SWEET:
bone dry | dry | off dry | medium sweet | sweet | very sweet

BODY:
very light | light | medium | medium-full | full-bodied | heavy

ACIDITY:
tart | crisp | fresh | smooth | flabby

TANNINS (IF PRESENT):
LEVEL: low | medium | high   TYPE: soft | round | dry | hard

BALANCE:
good | fair | unbalanced (excess: alcohol - acid - tannin - sugar)

FLAVOR INTENSITY:
low | moderate | flavorful | powerful

FLAVORS:

FINISH:
short (< 3 sec) | medium (4-5) | long (5-7) | v. long (>8 sec)

CONCLUSION:

STYLE:
traditional | in-between | modern

rating: ☆ ☆ ☆ ☆ ☆

FOOD: **FOOD PAIRING:**
                    MATCH: perfect | good | neutral | bad

tasting date: location:

tasting partner(s):

wine name:

producer:

region/appellation:

grape varieties:

vintage: alcohol: price:

 COLOR DEPTH:
watery | pale | medium | deep | dark

COLOR HUE:
WHITE: greenish | yellow | straw yellow | gold | amber
RED: purplish | ruby | red | garnet | brick | brown
ROSÉ: pink | salmon | orange | copper

CLARITY:
clear | slight haze | cloudy

 AROMA INTENSITY:
low | moderate | aromatic | powerful

DEVELOPMENT:
youthful | some age | aged

AROMAS:

 DRY/SWEET:
bone dry | dry | off dry | medium sweet | sweet | very sweet

BODY:
very light | light | medium | medium-full | full-bodied | heavy

ACIDITY:
tart | crisp | fresh | smooth | flabby

TANNINS (IF PRESENT):
LEVEL: low | medium | high   TYPE: soft | round | dry | hard

BALANCE:
good | fair | unbalanced (excess: alcohol - acid - tannin - sugar)

FLAVOR INTENSITY:
low | moderate | flavorful | powerful

FLAVORS:

FINISH:
short (< 3 sec) | medium (4-5) | long (5-7) | v. long (>8 sec)

CONCLUSION:

STYLE:
traditional | in-between | modern

rating: ☆ ☆ ☆ ☆ ☆

FOOD: **FOOD PAIRING:**
MATCH: perfect | good | neutral | bad

tasting date: location:

tasting partner(s):

wine name:

producer:

region/appellation:

grape varieties:

vintage: alcohol: price:

COLOR DEPTH:
watery | pale | medium | deep | dark

COLOR HUE:
WHITE: greenish | yellow | straw yellow | gold | amber
RED: purplish | ruby | red | garnet | brick | brown
ROSÉ: pink | salmon | orange | copper

CLARITY:
clear | slight haze | cloudy

AROMA INTENSITY:
low | moderate | aromatic | powerful

DEVELOPMENT:
youthful | some age | aged

AROMAS:

DRY/SWEET:
bone dry | dry | off dry | medium sweet | sweet | very sweet

BODY:
very light | light | medium | medium-full | full-bodied | heavy

ACIDITY:
tart | crisp | fresh | smooth | flabby

TANNINS (IF PRESENT):
LEVEL: low | medium | high   TYPE: soft | round | dry | hard

BALANCE:
good | fair | unbalanced (excess: alcohol - acid - tannin - sugar)

FLAVOR INTENSITY:
low | moderate | flavorful | powerful

FLAVORS:

FINISH:
short (< 3 sec) | medium (4-5) | long (5-7) | v. long (>8 sec)

CONCLUSION:

STYLE:
traditional | in-between | modern

rating: ☆☆☆☆☆

FOOD: **FOOD PAIRING:**
MATCH: perfect | good | neutral | bad

tasting date: location:

tasting partner(s):

wine name:

producer:

region/appellation:

grape varieties:

vintage: alcohol: price:

COLOR DEPTH:
watery | pale | medium | deep | dark

COLOR HUE:
WHITE: greenish | yellow | straw yellow | gold | amber
RED: purplish | ruby | red | garnet | brick | brown
ROSÉ: pink | salmon | orange | copper

CLARITY:
clear | slight haze | cloudy

AROMA INTENSITY:
low | moderate | aromatic | powerful

DEVELOPMENT:
youthful | some age | aged

AROMAS:

DRY/SWEET:
bone dry | dry | off dry | medium sweet | sweet | very sweet

BODY:
very light | light | medium | medium-full | full-bodied | heavy

ACIDITY:
tart | crisp | fresh | smooth | flabby

TANNINS (IF PRESENT):
LEVEL: low | medium | high   TYPE: soft | round | dry | hard

BALANCE:
good | fair | unbalanced (excess: alcohol - acid - tannin - sugar)

FLAVOR INTENSITY:
low | moderate | flavorful | powerful

FLAVORS:

FINISH:
short (< 3 sec) | medium (4-5) | long (5-7) | v. long (>8 sec)

CONCLUSION:

STYLE:
traditional | in-between | modern

rating: ☆ ☆ ☆ ☆ ☆

FOOD: **FOOD PAIRING:**

MATCH: perfect | good | neutral | bad

tasting date: location:

tasting partner(s):

wine name:

producer:

region/appellation:

grape varieties:

vintage: alcohol: price:

COLOR DEPTH:
watery | pale | medium | deep | dark

COLOR HUE:
WHITE: greenish | yellow | straw yellow | gold | amber
RED: purplish | ruby | red | garnet | brick | brown
ROSÉ: pink | salmon | orange | copper

CLARITY:
clear | slight haze | cloudy

AROMA INTENSITY:
low | moderate | aromatic | powerful

DEVELOPMENT:
youthful | some age | aged

AROMAS:

DRY/SWEET:
bone dry | dry | off dry | medium sweet | sweet | very sweet

BODY:
very light | light | medium | medium-full | full-bodied | heavy

ACIDITY:
tart | crisp | fresh | smooth | flabby

TANNINS (IF PRESENT):
LEVEL: low | medium | high   TYPE: soft | round | dry | hard

BALANCE:
good | fair | unbalanced (excess: alcohol - acid - tannin - sugar)

FLAVOR INTENSITY:
low | moderate | flavorful | powerful

FLAVORS:

FINISH:
short (< 3 sec) | medium (4-5) | long (5-7) | v. long (>8 sec)

CONCLUSION:

STYLE:
traditional | in-between | modern

rating: ☆ ☆ ☆ ☆ ☆

FOOD: ## FOOD PAIRING:
MATCH: perfect | good | neutral | bad

tasting date: location:

tasting partner(s):

wine name:

producer:

region/appellation:

grape varieties:

vintage: alcohol: price:

COLOR DEPTH:
watery | pale | medium | deep | dark

COLOR HUE:
WHITE: greenish | yellow | straw yellow | gold | amber
RED: purplish | ruby | red | garnet | brick | brown
ROSÉ: pink | salmon | orange | copper

CLARITY:
clear | slight haze | cloudy

AROMA INTENSITY:
low | moderate | aromatic | powerful

DEVELOPMENT:
youthful | some age | aged

AROMAS:

DRY/SWEET:
bone dry | dry | off dry | medium sweet | sweet | very sweet

BODY:
very light | light | medium | medium-full | full-bodied | heavy

ACIDITY:
tart | crisp | fresh | smooth | flabby

TANNINS (IF PRESENT):
LEVEL: low | medium | high   TYPE: soft | round | dry | hard

BALANCE:
good | fair | unbalanced (excess: alcohol - acid - tannin - sugar)

FLAVOR INTENSITY:
low | moderate | flavorful | powerful

FLAVORS:

FINISH:
short (< 3 sec) | medium (4-5) | long (5-7) | v. long (>8 sec)

CONCLUSION:

STYLE:
traditional | in-between | modern

rating: ☆ ☆ ☆ ☆ ☆

FOOD: ### FOOD PAIRING:
                  MATCH: perfect | good | neutral | bad

tasting date: location:

tasting partner(s):

wine name:

producer:

region/appellation:

grape varieties:

vintage: alcohol: price:

COLOR DEPTH:
watery | pale | medium | deep | dark
COLOR HUE:
WHITE: greenish | yellow | straw yellow | gold | amber
RED: purplish | ruby | red | garnet | brick | brown
ROSÉ: pink | salmon | orange | copper
CLARITY:
clear | slight haze | cloudy

AROMA INTENSITY:
low | moderate | aromatic | powerful
DEVELOPMENT:
youthful | some age | aged
AROMAS:

DRY/SWEET:
bone dry | dry | off dry | medium sweet | sweet | very sweet
BODY:
very light | light | medium | medium-full | full-bodied | heavy
ACIDITY:
tart | crisp | fresh | smooth | flabby
TANNINS (IF PRESENT):
LEVEL: low | medium | high   TYPE: soft | round | dry | hard
BALANCE:
good | fair | unbalanced (excess: alcohol - acid - tannin - sugar)
FLAVOR INTENSITY:
low | moderate | flavorful | powerful
FLAVORS:

FINISH:
short (< 3 sec) | medium (4-5) | long (5-7) | v. long (>8 sec)

CONCLUSION:

STYLE:
traditional | in-between | modern

rating: ☆ ☆ ☆ ☆ ☆

FOOD: ### FOOD PAIRING:
MATCH: perfect | good | neutral | bad

tasting date: location:

tasting partner(s):

wine name:

producer:

region/appellation:

grape varieties:

vintage: alcohol: price:

COLOR DEPTH:
watery | pale | medium | deep | dark

COLOR HUE:
WHITE: greenish | yellow | straw yellow | gold | amber
RED: purplish | ruby | red | garnet | brick | brown
ROSÉ: pink | salmon | orange | copper

CLARITY:
clear | slight haze | cloudy

AROMA INTENSITY:
low | moderate | aromatic | powerful

DEVELOPMENT:
youthful | some age | aged

AROMAS:

DRY/SWEET:
bone dry | dry | off dry | medium sweet | sweet | very sweet

BODY:
very light | light | medium | medium-full | full-bodied | heavy

ACIDITY:
tart | crisp | fresh | smooth | flabby

TANNINS (IF PRESENT):
LEVEL: low | medium | high   TYPE: soft | round | dry | hard

BALANCE:
good | fair | unbalanced (excess: alcohol - acid - tannin - sugar)

FLAVOR INTENSITY:
low | moderate | flavorful | powerful

FLAVORS:

FINISH:
short (< 3 sec) | medium (4-5) | long (5-7) | v. long (>8 sec)

CONCLUSION:

STYLE:
traditional | in-between | modern

rating: ☆ ☆ ☆ ☆ ☆

FOOD: **FOOD PAIRING:**

MATCH: perfect | good | neutral | bad

tasting date: location:

tasting partner(s):

wine name:

producer:

region/appellation:

grape varieties:

vintage: alcohol: price:

COLOR DEPTH:
watery | pale | medium | deep | dark
COLOR HUE:
WHITE: greenish | yellow | straw yellow | gold | amber
RED: purplish | ruby | red | garnet | brick | brown
ROSÉ: pink | salmon | orange | copper
CLARITY:
clear | slight haze | cloudy

AROMA INTENSITY:
low | moderate | aromatic | powerful
DEVELOPMENT:
youthful | some age | aged
AROMAS:

DRY/SWEET:
bone dry | dry | off dry | medium sweet | sweet | very sweet
BODY:
very light | light | medium | medium-full | full-bodied | heavy
ACIDITY:
tart | crisp | fresh | smooth | flabby
TANNINS (IF PRESENT):
LEVEL: low | medium | high   TYPE: soft | round | dry | hard
BALANCE:
good | fair | unbalanced (excess: alcohol - acid - tannin - sugar)
FLAVOR INTENSITY:
low | moderate | flavorful | powerful
FLAVORS:

FINISH:
short (< 3 sec) | medium (4-5) | long (5-7) | v. long (>8 sec)
CONCLUSION:

STYLE:
traditional | in-between | modern
rating: ☆ ☆ ☆ ☆ ☆

FOOD: **FOOD PAIRING:**
                    MATCH: perfect | good | neutral | bad

tasting date: location:

tasting partner(s):

wine name:

producer:

region/appellation:

grape varieties:

vintage: alcohol: price:

COLOR DEPTH:
watery | pale | medium | deep | dark

COLOR HUE:
WHITE: greenish | yellow | straw yellow | gold | amber
RED: purplish | ruby | red | garnet | brick | brown
ROSÉ: pink | salmon | orange | copper

CLARITY:
clear | slight haze | cloudy

AROMA INTENSITY:
low | moderate | aromatic | powerful

DEVELOPMENT:
youthful | some age | aged

AROMAS:

DRY/SWEET:
bone dry | dry | off dry | medium sweet | sweet | very sweet

BODY:
very light | light | medium | medium-full | full-bodied | heavy

ACIDITY:
tart | crisp | fresh | smooth | flabby

TANNINS (IF PRESENT):
LEVEL: low | medium | high   TYPE: soft | round | dry | hard

BALANCE:
good | fair | unbalanced (excess: alcohol - acid - tannin - sugar)

FLAVOR INTENSITY:
low | moderate | flavorful | powerful

FLAVORS:

FINISH:
short (< 3 sec) | medium (4-5) | long (5-7) | v. long (>8 sec)

CONCLUSION:

STYLE:
traditional | in-between | modern

rating: ☆ ☆ ☆ ☆ ☆

FOOD: **FOOD PAIRING:**
                MATCH: perfect | good | neutral | bad

tasting date: location:

tasting partner(s):

wine name:

producer:

region/appellation:

grape varieties:

vintage: alcohol: price:

COLOR DEPTH:
watery | pale | medium | deep | dark

COLOR HUE:
WHITE: greenish | yellow | straw yellow | gold | amber
RED: purplish | ruby | red | garnet | brick | brown
ROSÉ: pink | salmon | orange | copper

CLARITY:
clear | slight haze | cloudy

AROMA INTENSITY:
low | moderate | aromatic | powerful

DEVELOPMENT:
youthful | some age | aged

AROMAS:

DRY/SWEET:
bone dry | dry | off dry | medium sweet | sweet | very sweet

BODY:
very light | light | medium | medium-full | full-bodied | heavy

ACIDITY:
tart | crisp | fresh | smooth | flabby

TANNINS (IF PRESENT):
LEVEL: low | medium | high   TYPE: soft | round | dry | hard

BALANCE:
good | fair | unbalanced (excess: alcohol - acid - tannin - sugar)

FLAVOR INTENSITY:
low | moderate | flavorful | powerful

FLAVORS:

FINISH:
short (< 3 sec) | medium (4-5) | long (5-7) | v. long (>8 sec)

CONCLUSION:

STYLE:
traditional | in-between | modern

rating: ☆ ☆ ☆ ☆ ☆

FOOD: ## FOOD PAIRING:
MATCH: perfect | good | neutral | bad

tasting date: location:

tasting partner(s):

wine name:

producer:

region/appellation:

grape varieties:

vintage: alcohol: price:

COLOR DEPTH:
watery | pale | medium | deep | dark

COLOR HUE:
WHITE: greenish | yellow | straw yellow | gold | amber
RED: purplish | ruby | red | garnet | brick | brown
ROSÉ: pink | salmon | orange | copper

CLARITY:
clear | slight haze | cloudy

AROMA INTENSITY:
low | moderate | aromatic | powerful

DEVELOPMENT:
youthful | some age | aged

AROMAS:

DRY/SWEET:
bone dry | dry | off dry | medium sweet | sweet | very sweet

BODY:
very light | light | medium | medium-full | full-bodied | heavy

ACIDITY:
tart | crisp | fresh | smooth | flabby

TANNINS (IF PRESENT):
LEVEL: low | medium | high   TYPE: soft | round | dry | hard

BALANCE:
good | fair | unbalanced (excess: alcohol - acid - tannin - sugar)

FLAVOR INTENSITY:
low | moderate | flavorful | powerful

FLAVORS:

FINISH:
short (< 3 sec) | medium (4-5) | long (5-7) | v. long (>8 sec)

CONCLUSION:

STYLE:
traditional | in-between | modern

rating: ☆ ☆ ☆ ☆ ☆

FOOD: **FOOD PAIRING:**
MATCH: perfect | good | neutral | bad

tasting date: location:

tasting partner(s):

wine name:

producer:

region/appellation:

grape varieties:

vintage: alcohol: price:

COLOR DEPTH:
watery | pale | medium | deep | dark

COLOR HUE:
WHITE: greenish | yellow | straw yellow | gold | amber
RED: purplish | ruby | red | garnet | brick | brown
ROSÉ: pink | salmon | orange | copper

CLARITY:
clear | slight haze | cloudy

AROMA INTENSITY:
low | moderate | aromatic | powerful

DEVELOPMENT:
youthful | some age | aged

AROMAS:

DRY/SWEET:
bone dry | dry | off dry | medium sweet | sweet | very sweet

BODY:
very light | light | medium | medium-full | full-bodied | heavy

ACIDITY:
tart | crisp | fresh | smooth | flabby

TANNINS (IF PRESENT):
LEVEL: low | medium | high   TYPE: soft | round | dry | hard

BALANCE:
good | fair | unbalanced (excess: alcohol - acid - tannin - sugar)

FLAVOR INTENSITY:
low | moderate | flavorful | powerful

FLAVORS:

FINISH:
short (< 3 sec) | medium (4-5) | long (5-7) | v. long (>8 sec)

CONCLUSION:

STYLE:
traditional | in-between | modern

rating: ☆ ☆ ☆ ☆ ☆

FOOD: **FOOD PAIRING:**
                        MATCH: perfect | good | neutral | bad

tasting date: location:

tasting partner(s):

wine name:

producer:

region/appellation:

grape varieties:

vintage: alcohol: price:

COLOR DEPTH:
watery | pale | medium | deep | dark

COLOR HUE:
WHITE: greenish | yellow | straw yellow | gold | amber
RED: purplish | ruby | red | garnet | brick | brown
ROSÉ: pink | salmon | orange | copper

CLARITY:
clear | slight haze | cloudy

AROMA INTENSITY:
low | moderate | aromatic | powerful

DEVELOPMENT:
youthful | some age | aged

AROMAS:

DRY/SWEET:
bone dry | dry | off dry | medium sweet | sweet | very sweet

BODY:
very light | light | medium | medium-full | full-bodied | heavy

ACIDITY:
tart | crisp | fresh | smooth | flabby

TANNINS (IF PRESENT):
LEVEL: low | medium | high   TYPE: soft | round | dry | hard

BALANCE:
good | fair | unbalanced (excess: alcohol - acid - tannin - sugar)

FLAVOR INTENSITY:
low | moderate | flavorful | powerful

FLAVORS:

FINISH:
short (< 3 sec) | medium (4-5) | long (5-7) | v. long (>8 sec)

CONCLUSION:

STYLE:
traditional | in-between | modern

rating: ☆ ☆ ☆ ☆ ☆

FOOD: ## FOOD PAIRING:
MATCH: perfect | good | neutral | bad

tasting date: location:

tasting partner(s):

wine name:

producer:

region/appellation:

grape varieties:

vintage: alcohol: price:

COLOR DEPTH:
watery | pale | medium | deep | dark

COLOR HUE:
WHITE: greenish | yellow | straw yellow | gold | amber
RED: purplish | ruby | red | garnet | brick | brown
ROSÉ: pink | salmon | orange | copper

CLARITY:
clear | slight haze | cloudy

AROMA INTENSITY:
low | moderate | aromatic | powerful

DEVELOPMENT:
youthful | some age | aged

AROMAS:

DRY/SWEET:
bone dry | dry | off dry | medium sweet | sweet | very sweet

BODY:
very light | light | medium | medium-full | full-bodied | heavy

ACIDITY:
tart | crisp | fresh | smooth | flabby

TANNINS (IF PRESENT):
LEVEL: low | medium | high   TYPE: soft | round | dry | hard

BALANCE:
good | fair | unbalanced (excess: alcohol - acid - tannin - sugar)

FLAVOR INTENSITY:
low | moderate | flavorful | powerful

FLAVORS:

FINISH:
short (< 3 sec) | medium (4-5) | long (5-7) | v. long (>8 sec)

CONCLUSION:

STYLE:
traditional | in-between | modern

rating: ☆ ☆ ☆ ☆ ☆

FOOD: ## FOOD PAIRING:
MATCH: perfect | good | neutral | bad

tasting date: location:

tasting partner(s):

wine name:

producer:

region/appellation:

grape varieties:

vintage: alcohol: price:

 COLOR DEPTH:
watery | pale | medium | deep | dark

COLOR HUE:
WHITE: greenish | yellow | straw yellow | gold | amber
RED: purplish | ruby | red | garnet | brick | brown
ROSÉ: pink | salmon | orange | copper

CLARITY:
clear | slight haze | cloudy

 AROMA INTENSITY:
low | moderate | aromatic | powerful

DEVELOPMENT:
youthful | some age | aged

AROMAS:

 DRY/SWEET:
bone dry | dry | off dry | medium sweet | sweet | very sweet

BODY:
very light | light | medium | medium-full | full-bodied | heavy

ACIDITY:
tart | crisp | fresh | smooth | flabby

TANNINS (IF PRESENT):
LEVEL: low | medium | high   TYPE: soft | round | dry | hard

BALANCE:
good | fair | unbalanced (excess: alcohol - acid - tannin - sugar)

FLAVOR INTENSITY:
low | moderate | flavorful | powerful

FLAVORS:

FINISH:
short (< 3 sec) | medium (4-5) | long (5-7) | v. long (>8 sec)

CONCLUSION:

STYLE:
traditional | in-between | modern

rating: ☆ ☆ ☆ ☆ ☆

FOOD: **FOOD PAIRING:**
                    MATCH: perfect | good | neutral | bad

tasting date: location:

tasting partner(s):

wine name:

producer:

region/appellation:

grape varieties:

vintage: alcohol: price:

COLOR DEPTH:
watery | pale | medium | deep | dark

COLOR HUE:
WHITE: greenish | yellow | straw yellow | gold | amber
RED: purplish | ruby | red | garnet | brick | brown
ROSÉ: pink | salmon | orange | copper

CLARITY:
clear | slight haze | cloudy

AROMA INTENSITY:
low | moderate | aromatic | powerful

DEVELOPMENT:
youthful | some age | aged

AROMAS:

DRY/SWEET:
bone dry | dry | off dry | medium sweet | sweet | very sweet

BODY:
very light | light | medium | medium-full | full-bodied | heavy

ACIDITY:
tart | crisp | fresh | smooth | flabby

TANNINS (IF PRESENT):
LEVEL: low | medium | high   TYPE: soft | round | dry | hard

BALANCE:
good | fair | unbalanced (excess: alcohol - acid - tannin - sugar)

FLAVOR INTENSITY:
low | moderate | flavorful | powerful

FLAVORS:

FINISH:
short (< 3 sec) | medium (4-5) | long (5-7) | v. long (>8 sec)

CONCLUSION:

STYLE:
traditional | in-between | modern

rating: ☆ ☆ ☆ ☆ ☆

FOOD: **FOOD PAIRING:**

MATCH: perfect | good | neutral | bad

tasting date: location:

tasting partner(s):

wine name:

producer:

region/appellation:

grape varieties:

vintage: alcohol: price:

COLOR DEPTH:
watery | pale | medium | deep | dark

COLOR HUE:
WHITE: greenish | yellow | straw yellow | gold | amber
RED: purplish | ruby | red | garnet | brick | brown
ROSÉ: pink | salmon | orange | copper

CLARITY:
clear | slight haze | cloudy

AROMA INTENSITY:
low | moderate | aromatic | powerful

DEVELOPMENT:
youthful | some age | aged

AROMAS:

DRY/SWEET:
bone dry | dry | off dry | medium sweet | sweet | very sweet

BODY:
very light | light | medium | medium-full | full-bodied | heavy

ACIDITY:
tart | crisp | fresh | smooth | flabby

TANNINS (IF PRESENT):
LEVEL: low | medium | high   TYPE: soft | round | dry | hard

BALANCE:
good | fair | unbalanced (excess: alcohol - acid - tannin - sugar)

FLAVOR INTENSITY:
low | moderate | flavorful | powerful

FLAVORS:

FINISH:
short (< 3 sec) | medium (4-5) | long (5-7) | v. long (>8 sec)

CONCLUSION:

STYLE:
traditional | in-between | modern

rating: ☆ ☆ ☆ ☆ ☆

FOOD: ### FOOD PAIRING:
MATCH: perfect | good | neutral | bad

tasting date: location:

tasting partner(s):

wine name:

producer:

region/appellation:

grape varieties:

vintage: alcohol: price:

 COLOR DEPTH:
watery | pale | medium | deep | dark

COLOR HUE:
WHITE: greenish | yellow | straw yellow | gold | amber
RED: purplish | ruby | red | garnet | brick | brown
ROSÉ: pink | salmon | orange | copper

CLARITY:
clear | slight haze | cloudy

AROMA INTENSITY:
low | moderate | aromatic | powerful

DEVELOPMENT:
youthful | some age | aged

AROMAS:

DRY/SWEET:
bone dry | dry | off dry | medium sweet | sweet | very sweet

BODY:
very light | light | medium | medium-full | full-bodied | heavy

ACIDITY:
tart | crisp | fresh | smooth | flabby

TANNINS (IF PRESENT):
LEVEL: low | medium | high   TYPE: soft | round | dry | hard

BALANCE:
good | fair | unbalanced (excess: alcohol - acid - tannin - sugar)

FLAVOR INTENSITY:
low | moderate | flavorful | powerful

FLAVORS:

FINISH:
short (< 3 sec) | medium (4-5) | long (5-7) | v. long (>8 sec)

CONCLUSION:

STYLE:
traditional | in-between | modern

rating: ☆ ☆ ☆ ☆ ☆

FOOD: **FOOD PAIRING:**
MATCH: perfect | good | neutral | bad

tasting date: location:

tasting partner(s):

wine name:

producer:

region/appellation:

grape varieties:

vintage: alcohol: price:

COLOR DEPTH:
watery | pale | medium | deep | dark

COLOR HUE:
WHITE: greenish | yellow | straw yellow | gold | amber
RED: purplish | ruby | red | garnet | brick | brown
ROSÉ: pink | salmon | orange | copper

CLARITY:
clear | slight haze | cloudy

AROMA INTENSITY:
low | moderate | aromatic | powerful

DEVELOPMENT:
youthful | some age | aged

AROMAS:

DRY/SWEET:
bone dry | dry | off dry | medium sweet | sweet | very sweet

BODY:
very light | light | medium | medium-full | full-bodied | heavy

ACIDITY:
tart | crisp | fresh | smooth | flabby

TANNINS (IF PRESENT):
LEVEL: low | medium | high   TYPE: soft | round | dry | hard

BALANCE:
good | fair | unbalanced (excess: alcohol - acid - tannin - sugar)

FLAVOR INTENSITY:
low | moderate | flavorful | powerful

FLAVORS:

FINISH:
short (< 3 sec) | medium (4-5) | long (5-7) | v. long (>8 sec)

CONCLUSION:

STYLE:
traditional | in-between | modern

rating: ☆ ☆ ☆ ☆ ☆

FOOD: **FOOD PAIRING:**

MATCH: perfect | good | neutral | bad

tasting date: location:

tasting partner(s):

wine name:

producer:

region/appellation:

grape varieties:

vintage: alcohol: price:

COLOR DEPTH:
watery | pale | medium | deep | dark

COLOR HUE:
WHITE: greenish | yellow | straw yellow | gold | amber
RED: purplish | ruby | red | garnet | brick | brown
ROSÉ: pink | salmon | orange | copper

CLARITY:
clear | slight haze | cloudy

AROMA INTENSITY:
low | moderate | aromatic | powerful

DEVELOPMENT:
youthful | some age | aged

AROMAS:

DRY/SWEET:
bone dry | dry | off dry | medium sweet | sweet | very sweet

BODY:
very light | light | medium | medium-full | full-bodied | heavy

ACIDITY:
tart | crisp | fresh | smooth | flabby

TANNINS (IF PRESENT):
LEVEL: low | medium | high   TYPE: soft | round | dry | hard

BALANCE:
good | fair | unbalanced (excess: alcohol - acid - tannin - sugar)

FLAVOR INTENSITY:
low | moderate | flavorful | powerful

FLAVORS:

FINISH:
short (< 3 sec) | medium (4-5) | long (5-7) | v. long (>8 sec)

CONCLUSION:

STYLE:
traditional | in-between | modern

rating: ☆ ☆ ☆ ☆ ☆

FOOD: ## FOOD PAIRING:
MATCH: perfect | good | neutral | bad

tasting date: location:

tasting partner(s):

wine name:

producer:

region/appellation:

grape varieties:

vintage: alcohol: price:

COLOR DEPTH:
watery | pale | medium | deep | dark

COLOR HUE:
WHITE: greenish | yellow | straw yellow | gold | amber
RED: purplish | ruby | red | garnet | brick | brown
ROSÉ: pink | salmon | orange | copper

CLARITY:
clear | slight haze | cloudy

AROMA INTENSITY:
low | moderate | aromatic | powerful

DEVELOPMENT:
youthful | some age | aged

AROMAS:

DRY/SWEET:
bone dry | dry | off dry | medium sweet | sweet | very sweet

BODY:
very light | light | medium | medium-full | full-bodied | heavy

ACIDITY:
tart | crisp | fresh | smooth | flabby

TANNINS (IF PRESENT):
LEVEL: low | medium | high   TYPE: soft | round | dry | hard

BALANCE:
good | fair | unbalanced (excess: alcohol - acid - tannin - sugar)

FLAVOR INTENSITY:
low | moderate | flavorful | powerful

FLAVORS:

FINISH:
short (< 3 sec) | medium (4-5) | long (5-7) | v. long (>8 sec)

CONCLUSION:

STYLE:
traditional | in-between | modern

rating: ☆ ☆ ☆ ☆ ☆

FOOD: **FOOD PAIRING:**
                MATCH: perfect | good | neutral | bad

tasting date: location:

tasting partner(s):

wine name:

producer:

region/appellation:

grape varieties:

vintage: alcohol: price:

COLOR DEPTH:
watery | pale | medium | deep | dark

COLOR HUE:
WHITE: greenish | yellow | straw yellow | gold | amber
RED: purplish | ruby | red | garnet | brick | brown
ROSÉ: pink | salmon | orange | copper

CLARITY:
clear | slight haze | cloudy

AROMA INTENSITY:
low | moderate | aromatic | powerful

DEVELOPMENT:
youthful | some age | aged

AROMAS:

DRY/SWEET:
bone dry | dry | off dry | medium sweet | sweet | very sweet

BODY:
very light | light | medium | medium-full | full-bodied | heavy

ACIDITY:
tart | crisp | fresh | smooth | flabby

TANNINS (IF PRESENT):
LEVEL: low | medium | high   TYPE: soft | round | dry | hard

BALANCE:
good | fair | unbalanced (excess: alcohol - acid - tannin - sugar)

FLAVOR INTENSITY:
low | moderate | flavorful | powerful

FLAVORS:

FINISH:
short (< 3 sec) | medium (4-5) | long (5-7) | v. long (>8 sec)

CONCLUSION:

STYLE:
traditional | in-between | modern

rating: ☆ ☆ ☆ ☆ ☆

FOOD: **FOOD PAIRING:**
                MATCH: perfect | good | neutral | bad

tasting date: location:

tasting partner(s):

wine name:

producer:

region/appellation:

grape varieties:

vintage: alcohol: price:

COLOR DEPTH:
watery | pale | medium | deep | dark

COLOR HUE:
WHITE: greenish | yellow | straw yellow | gold | amber
RED: purplish | ruby | red | garnet | brick | brown
ROSÉ: pink | salmon | orange | copper

CLARITY:
clear | slight haze | cloudy

AROMA INTENSITY:
low | moderate | aromatic | powerful

DEVELOPMENT:
youthful | some age | aged

AROMAS:

DRY/SWEET:
bone dry | dry | off dry | medium sweet | sweet | very sweet

BODY:
very light | light | medium | medium-full | full-bodied | heavy

ACIDITY:
tart | crisp | fresh | smooth | flabby

TANNINS (IF PRESENT):
LEVEL: low | medium | high   TYPE: soft | round | dry | hard

BALANCE:
good | fair | unbalanced (excess: alcohol - acid - tannin - sugar)

FLAVOR INTENSITY:
low | moderate | flavorful | powerful

FLAVORS:

FINISH:
short (< 3 sec) | medium (4-5) | long (5-7) | v. long (>8 sec)

CONCLUSION:

STYLE:
traditional | in-between | modern

rating: ☆ ☆ ☆ ☆ ☆

FOOD: **FOOD PAIRING:**

MATCH: perfect | good | neutral | bad

tasting date: location:

tasting partner(s):

wine name:

producer:

region/appellation:

grape varieties:

vintage: alcohol: price:

COLOR DEPTH:
watery | pale | medium | deep | dark

COLOR HUE:
WHITE: greenish | yellow | straw yellow | gold | amber
RED: purplish | ruby | red | garnet | brick | brown
ROSÉ: pink | salmon | orange | copper

CLARITY:
clear | slight haze | cloudy

AROMA INTENSITY:
low | moderate | aromatic | powerful

DEVELOPMENT:
youthful | some age | aged

AROMAS:

DRY/SWEET:
bone dry | dry | off dry | medium sweet | sweet | very sweet

BODY:
very light | light | medium | medium-full | full-bodied | heavy

ACIDITY:
tart | crisp | fresh | smooth | flabby

TANNINS (IF PRESENT):
LEVEL: low | medium | high   TYPE: soft | round | dry | hard

BALANCE:
good | fair | unbalanced (excess: alcohol - acid - tannin - sugar)

FLAVOR INTENSITY:
low | moderate | flavorful | powerful

FLAVORS:

FINISH:
short (< 3 sec) | medium (4-5) | long (5-7) | v. long (>8 sec)

CONCLUSION:

STYLE:
traditional | in-between | modern

rating: ☆ ☆ ☆ ☆ ☆

FOOD: **FOOD PAIRING:**
                    MATCH: perfect | good | neutral | bad

tasting date: location:

tasting partner(s):

wine name:

producer:

region/appellation:

grape varieties:

vintage: alcohol: price:

COLOR DEPTH:
watery | pale | medium | deep | dark

COLOR HUE:
WHITE: greenish | yellow | straw yellow | gold | amber
RED: purplish | ruby | red | garnet | brick | brown
ROSÉ: pink | salmon | orange | copper

CLARITY:
clear | slight haze | cloudy

AROMA INTENSITY:
low | moderate | aromatic | powerful

DEVELOPMENT:
youthful | some age | aged

AROMAS:

DRY/SWEET:
bone dry | dry | off dry | medium sweet | sweet | very sweet

BODY:
very light | light | medium | medium-full | full-bodied | heavy

ACIDITY:
tart | crisp | fresh | smooth | flabby

TANNINS (IF PRESENT):
LEVEL: low | medium | high   TYPE: soft | round | dry | hard

BALANCE:
good | fair | unbalanced (excess: alcohol - acid - tannin - sugar)

FLAVOR INTENSITY:
low | moderate | flavorful | powerful

FLAVORS:

FINISH:
short (< 3 sec) | medium (4-5) | long (5-7) | v. long (>8 sec)

CONCLUSION:

STYLE:
traditional | in-between | modern

rating: ☆ ☆ ☆ ☆ ☆

FOOD: **FOOD PAIRING:**

MATCH: perfect | good | neutral | bad

tasting date: location:

tasting partner(s):

wine name:

producer:

region/appellation:

grape varieties:

vintage: alcohol: price:

COLOR DEPTH:
watery | pale | medium | deep | dark

COLOR HUE:
WHITE: greenish | yellow | straw yellow | gold | amber
RED: purplish | ruby | red | garnet | brick | brown
ROSÉ: pink | salmon | orange | copper

CLARITY:
clear | slight haze | cloudy

AROMA INTENSITY:
low | moderate | aromatic | powerful

DEVELOPMENT:
youthful | some age | aged

AROMAS:

DRY/SWEET:
bone dry | dry | off dry | medium sweet | sweet | very sweet

BODY:
very light | light | medium | medium-full | full-bodied | heavy

ACIDITY:
tart | crisp | fresh | smooth | flabby

TANNINS (IF PRESENT):
LEVEL: low | medium | high   TYPE: soft | round | dry | hard

BALANCE:
good | fair | unbalanced (excess: alcohol - acid - tannin - sugar)

FLAVOR INTENSITY:
low | moderate | flavorful | powerful

FLAVORS:

FINISH:
short (< 3 sec) | medium (4-5) | long (5-7) | v. long (>8 sec)

CONCLUSION:

STYLE:
traditional | in-between | modern

rating: ☆☆☆☆☆

FOOD: **FOOD PAIRING:**
                         MATCH: perfect | good | neutral | bad

tasting date: location:

tasting partner(s):

wine name:

producer:

region/appellation:

grape varieties:

vintage: alcohol: price:

COLOR DEPTH:
watery | pale | medium | deep | dark

COLOR HUE:
WHITE: greenish | yellow | straw yellow | gold | amber
RED: purplish | ruby | red | garnet | brick | brown
ROSÉ: pink | salmon | orange | copper

CLARITY:
clear | slight haze | cloudy

AROMA INTENSITY:
low | moderate | aromatic | powerful

DEVELOPMENT:
youthful | some age | aged

AROMAS:

DRY/SWEET:
bone dry | dry | off dry | medium sweet | sweet | very sweet

BODY:
very light | light | medium | medium-full | full-bodied | heavy

ACIDITY:
tart | crisp | fresh | smooth | flabby

TANNINS (IF PRESENT):
LEVEL: low | medium | high   TYPE: soft | round | dry | hard

BALANCE:
good | fair | unbalanced (excess: alcohol - acid - tannin - sugar)

FLAVOR INTENSITY:
low | moderate | flavorful | powerful

FLAVORS:

FINISH:
short (< 3 sec) | medium (4-5) | long (5-7) | v. long (>8 sec)

CONCLUSION:

STYLE:
traditional | in-between | modern

rating: ☆ ☆ ☆ ☆ ☆

FOOD: **FOOD PAIRING:**

MATCH: perfect | good | neutral | bad

tasting date: location:

tasting partner(s):

wine name:

producer:

region/appellation:

grape varieties:

vintage: alcohol: price:

COLOR DEPTH:
watery | pale | medium | deep | dark

COLOR HUE:
WHITE: greenish | yellow | straw yellow | gold | amber
RED: purplish | ruby | red | garnet | brick | brown
ROSÉ: pink | salmon | orange | copper

CLARITY:
clear | slight haze | cloudy

AROMA INTENSITY:
low | moderate | aromatic | powerful

DEVELOPMENT:
youthful | some age | aged

AROMAS:

DRY/SWEET:
bone dry | dry | off dry | medium sweet | sweet | very sweet

BODY:
very light | light | medium | medium-full | full-bodied | heavy

ACIDITY:
tart | crisp | fresh | smooth | flabby

TANNINS (IF PRESENT):
LEVEL: low | medium | high   TYPE: soft | round | dry | hard

BALANCE:
good | fair | unbalanced (excess: alcohol - acid - tannin - sugar)

FLAVOR INTENSITY:
low | moderate | flavorful | powerful

FLAVORS:

FINISH:
short (< 3 sec) | medium (4-5) | long (5-7) | v. long (>8 sec)

CONCLUSION:

STYLE:
traditional | in-between | modern

rating: ☆ ☆ ☆ ☆ ☆

FOOD: **FOOD PAIRING:**
MATCH: perfect | good | neutral | bad

tasting date: location:

tasting partner(s):

wine name:

producer:

region/appellation:

grape varieties:

vintage: alcohol: price:

 COLOR DEPTH:
watery | pale | medium | deep | dark

COLOR HUE:
WHITE: greenish | yellow | straw yellow | gold | amber
RED: purplish | ruby | red | garnet | brick | brown
ROSÉ: pink | salmon | orange | copper

CLARITY:
clear | slight haze | cloudy

 AROMA INTENSITY:
low | moderate | aromatic | powerful

DEVELOPMENT:
youthful | some age | aged

AROMAS:

 DRY/SWEET:
bone dry | dry | off dry | medium sweet | sweet | very sweet

BODY:
very light | light | medium | medium-full | full-bodied | heavy

ACIDITY:
tart | crisp | fresh | smooth | flabby

TANNINS (IF PRESENT):
LEVEL: low | medium | high   TYPE: soft | round | dry | hard

BALANCE:
good | fair | unbalanced (excess: alcohol - acid - tannin - sugar)

FLAVOR INTENSITY:
low | moderate | flavorful | powerful

FLAVORS:

FINISH:
short (< 3 sec) | medium (4-5) | long (5-7) | v. long (>8 sec)

CONCLUSION:

STYLE:
traditional | in-between | modern

rating: ☆ ☆ ☆ ☆ ☆

FOOD: **FOOD PAIRING:**
                   MATCH: perfect | good | neutral | bad

tasting date: location:

tasting partner(s):

wine name:

producer:

region/appellation:

grape varieties:

vintage: alcohol: price:

COLOR DEPTH:
watery | pale | medium | deep | dark

COLOR HUE:
WHITE: greenish | yellow | straw yellow | gold | amber
RED: purplish | ruby | red | garnet | brick | brown
ROSÉ: pink | salmon | orange | copper

CLARITY:
clear | slight haze | cloudy

AROMA INTENSITY:
low | moderate | aromatic | powerful

DEVELOPMENT:
youthful | some age | aged

AROMAS:

DRY/SWEET:
bone dry | dry | off dry | medium sweet | sweet | very sweet

BODY:
very light | light | medium | medium-full | full-bodied | heavy

ACIDITY:
tart | crisp | fresh | smooth | flabby

TANNINS (IF PRESENT):
LEVEL: low | medium | high   TYPE: soft | round | dry | hard

BALANCE:
good | fair | unbalanced (excess: alcohol - acid - tannin - sugar)

FLAVOR INTENSITY:
low | moderate | flavorful | powerful

FLAVORS:

FINISH:
short (< 3 sec) | medium (4-5) | long (5-7) | v. long (>8 sec)

CONCLUSION:

STYLE:
traditional | in-between | modern

rating: ☆ ☆ ☆ ☆ ☆

FOOD: **FOOD PAIRING:**
                    MATCH: perfect | good | neutral | bad

tasting date: location:

tasting partner(s):

wine name:

producer:

region/appellation:

grape varieties:

vintage: alcohol: price:

 COLOR DEPTH:
watery | pale | medium | deep | dark

COLOR HUE:
WHITE: greenish | yellow | straw yellow | gold | amber
RED: purplish | ruby | red | garnet | brick | brown
ROSÉ: pink | salmon | orange | copper

CLARITY:
clear | slight haze | cloudy

 AROMA INTENSITY:
low | moderate | aromatic | powerful

DEVELOPMENT:
youthful | some age | aged

AROMAS:

 DRY/SWEET:
bone dry | dry | off dry | medium sweet | sweet | very sweet

BODY:
very light | light | medium | medium-full | full-bodied | heavy

ACIDITY:
tart | crisp | fresh | smooth | flabby

TANNINS (IF PRESENT):
LEVEL: low | medium | high   TYPE: soft | round | dry | hard

BALANCE:
good | fair | unbalanced (excess: alcohol - acid - tannin - sugar)

FLAVOR INTENSITY:
low | moderate | flavorful | powerful

FLAVORS:

FINISH:
short (< 3 sec) | medium (4-5) | long (5-7) | v. long (>8 sec)

CONCLUSION:

STYLE:
traditional | in-between | modern

rating: ☆ ☆ ☆ ☆ ☆

FOOD: **FOOD PAIRING:**
MATCH: perfect | good | neutral | bad

tasting date: location:

tasting partner(s):

wine name:

producer:

region/appellation:

grape varieties:

vintage: alcohol: price:

COLOR DEPTH:
watery | pale | medium | deep | dark

COLOR HUE:
WHITE: greenish | yellow | straw yellow | gold | amber
RED: purplish | ruby | red | garnet | brick | brown
ROSÉ: pink | salmon | orange | copper

CLARITY:
clear | slight haze | cloudy

AROMA INTENSITY:
low | moderate | aromatic | powerful

DEVELOPMENT:
youthful | some age | aged

AROMAS:

DRY/SWEET:
bone dry | dry | off dry | medium sweet | sweet | very sweet

BODY:
very light | light | medium | medium-full | full-bodied | heavy

ACIDITY:
tart | crisp | fresh | smooth | flabby

TANNINS (IF PRESENT):
LEVEL: low | medium | high   TYPE: soft | round | dry | hard

BALANCE:
good | fair | unbalanced (excess: alcohol - acid - tannin - sugar)

FLAVOR INTENSITY:
low | moderate | flavorful | powerful

FLAVORS:

FINISH:
short (< 3 sec) | medium (4-5) | long (5-7) | v. long (>8 sec)

CONCLUSION:

STYLE:
traditional | in-between | modern

rating: ☆ ☆ ☆ ☆ ☆

FOOD: **FOOD PAIRING:**
MATCH: perfect | good | neutral | bad

tasting date: location:

tasting partner(s):

wine name:

producer:

region/appellation:

grape varieties:

vintage: alcohol: price:

COLOR DEPTH:
watery | pale | medium | deep | dark

COLOR HUE:
WHITE: greenish | yellow | straw yellow | gold | amber
RED: purplish | ruby | red | garnet | brick | brown
ROSÉ: pink | salmon | orange | copper

CLARITY:
clear | slight haze | cloudy

AROMA INTENSITY:
low | moderate | aromatic | powerful

DEVELOPMENT:
youthful | some age | aged

AROMAS:

DRY/SWEET:
bone dry | dry | off dry | medium sweet | sweet | very sweet

BODY:
very light | light | medium | medium-full | full-bodied | heavy

ACIDITY:
tart | crisp | fresh | smooth | flabby

TANNINS (IF PRESENT):
LEVEL: low | medium | high   TYPE: soft | round | dry | hard

BALANCE:
good | fair | unbalanced (excess: alcohol - acid - tannin - sugar)

FLAVOR INTENSITY:
low | moderate | flavorful | powerful

FLAVORS:

FINISH:
short (< 3 sec) | medium (4-5) | long (5-7) | v. long (>8 sec)

CONCLUSION:

STYLE:
traditional | in-between | modern

rating: ☆ ☆ ☆ ☆ ☆

FOOD: **FOOD PAIRING:**
              MATCH: perfect | good | neutral | bad

tasting date: location:

tasting partner(s):

wine name:

producer:

region/appellation:

grape varieties:

vintage: alcohol: price:

COLOR DEPTH:
watery | pale | medium | deep | dark
COLOR HUE:
WHITE: greenish | yellow | straw yellow | gold | amber
RED: purplish | ruby | red | garnet | brick | brown
ROSÉ: pink | salmon | orange | copper

CLARITY:
clear | slight haze | cloudy

AROMA INTENSITY:
low | moderate | aromatic | powerful
DEVELOPMENT:
youthful | some age | aged
AROMAS:

DRY/SWEET:
bone dry | dry | off dry | medium sweet | sweet | very sweet
BODY:
very light | light | medium | medium-full | full-bodied | heavy
ACIDITY:
tart | crisp | fresh | smooth | flabby
TANNINS (IF PRESENT):
LEVEL: low | medium | high   TYPE: soft | round | dry | hard
BALANCE:
good | fair | unbalanced (excess: alcohol - acid - tannin - sugar)
FLAVOR INTENSITY:
low | moderate | flavorful | powerful
FLAVORS:

FINISH:
short (< 3 sec) | medium (4-5) | long (5-7) | v. long (>8 sec)

CONCLUSION:

STYLE:
traditional | in-between | modern

rating: ☆ ☆ ☆ ☆ ☆

FOOD: ### FOOD PAIRING:
                MATCH: perfect | good | neutral | bad

tasting date: location:

tasting partner(s):

wine name:

producer:

region/appellation:

grape varieties:

vintage: alcohol: price:

COLOR DEPTH:
watery | pale | medium | deep | dark

COLOR HUE:
WHITE: greenish | yellow | straw yellow | gold | amber
RED: purplish | ruby | red | garnet | brick | brown
ROSÉ: pink | salmon | orange | copper

CLARITY:
clear | slight haze | cloudy

AROMA INTENSITY:
low | moderate | aromatic | powerful

DEVELOPMENT:
youthful | some age | aged

AROMAS:

DRY/SWEET:
bone dry | dry | off dry | medium sweet | sweet | very sweet

BODY:
very light | light | medium | medium-full | full-bodied | heavy

ACIDITY:
tart | crisp | fresh | smooth | flabby

TANNINS (IF PRESENT):
LEVEL: low | medium | high   TYPE: soft | round | dry | hard

BALANCE:
good | fair | unbalanced (excess: alcohol - acid - tannin - sugar)

FLAVOR INTENSITY:
low | moderate | flavorful | powerful

FLAVORS:

FINISH:
short (< 3 sec) | medium (4-5) | long (5-7) | v. long (>8 sec)

CONCLUSION:

STYLE:
traditional | in-between | modern

rating: ☆ ☆ ☆ ☆ ☆

FOOD: **FOOD PAIRING:**

MATCH: perfect | good | neutral | bad

tasting date: location:

tasting partner(s):

wine name:

producer:

region/appellation:

grape varieties:

vintage: alcohol: price:

COLOR DEPTH:
watery | pale | medium | deep | dark

COLOR HUE:
WHITE: greenish | yellow | straw yellow | gold | amber
RED: purplish | ruby | red | garnet | brick | brown
ROSÉ: pink | salmon | orange | copper

CLARITY:
clear | slight haze | cloudy

AROMA INTENSITY:
low | moderate | aromatic | powerful

DEVELOPMENT:
youthful | some age | aged

AROMAS:

DRY/SWEET:
bone dry | dry | off dry | medium sweet | sweet | very sweet

BODY:
very light | light | medium | medium-full | full-bodied | heavy

ACIDITY:
tart | crisp | fresh | smooth | flabby

TANNINS (IF PRESENT):
LEVEL: low | medium | high   TYPE: soft | round | dry | hard

BALANCE:
good | fair | unbalanced (excess: alcohol - acid - tannin - sugar)

FLAVOR INTENSITY:
low | moderate | flavorful | powerful

FLAVORS:

FINISH:
short (< 3 sec) | medium (4-5) | long (5-7) | v. long (>8 sec)

CONCLUSION:

STYLE:
traditional | in-between | modern

rating: ☆ ☆ ☆ ☆ ☆

FOOD: **FOOD PAIRING:**
                MATCH: perfect | good | neutral | bad

tasting date: location:

tasting partner(s):

wine name:

producer:

region/appellation:

grape varieties:

vintage: alcohol: price:

COLOR DEPTH:
watery | pale | medium | deep | dark

COLOR HUE:
WHITE: greenish | yellow | straw yellow | gold | amber
RED: purplish | ruby | red | garnet | brick | brown
ROSÉ: pink | salmon | orange | copper

CLARITY:
clear | slight haze | cloudy

AROMA INTENSITY:
low | moderate | aromatic | powerful

DEVELOPMENT:
youthful | some age | aged

AROMAS:

DRY/SWEET:
bone dry | dry | off dry | medium sweet | sweet | very sweet

BODY:
very light | light | medium | medium-full | full-bodied | heavy

ACIDITY:
tart | crisp | fresh | smooth | flabby

TANNINS (IF PRESENT):
LEVEL: low | medium | high   TYPE: soft | round | dry | hard

BALANCE:
good | fair | unbalanced (excess: alcohol - acid - tannin - sugar)

FLAVOR INTENSITY:
low | moderate | flavorful | powerful

FLAVORS:

FINISH:
short (< 3 sec) | medium (4-5) | long (5-7) | v. long (>8 sec)

CONCLUSION:

STYLE:
traditional | in-between | modern

rating: ☆ ☆ ☆ ☆ ☆

FOOD: **FOOD PAIRING:**

                   MATCH: perfect | good | neutral | bad

tasting date: location:

tasting partner(s):

wine name:

producer:

region/appellation:

grape varieties:

vintage: alcohol: price:

COLOR DEPTH:
watery | pale | medium | deep | dark

COLOR HUE:
WHITE: greenish | yellow | straw yellow | gold | amber
RED: purplish | ruby | red | garnet | brick | brown
ROSÉ: pink | salmon | orange | copper

CLARITY:
clear | slight haze | cloudy

AROMA INTENSITY:
low | moderate | aromatic | powerful

DEVELOPMENT:
youthful | some age | aged

AROMAS:

DRY/SWEET:
bone dry | dry | off dry | medium sweet | sweet | very sweet

BODY:
very light | light | medium | medium-full | full-bodied | heavy

ACIDITY:
tart | crisp | fresh | smooth | flabby

TANNINS (IF PRESENT):
LEVEL: low | medium | high   TYPE: soft | round | dry | hard

BALANCE:
good | fair | unbalanced (excess: alcohol - acid - tannin - sugar)

FLAVOR INTENSITY:
low | moderate | flavorful | powerful

FLAVORS:

FINISH:
short (< 3 sec) | medium (4-5) | long (5-7) | v. long (>8 sec)

CONCLUSION:

STYLE:
traditional | in-between | modern

rating: ☆ ☆ ☆ ☆ ☆

FOOD: **FOOD PAIRING:**
                   MATCH: perfect | good | neutral | bad

tasting date: location:

tasting partner(s):

wine name:

producer:

region/appellation:

grape varieties:

vintage: alcohol: price:

COLOR DEPTH:
watery | pale | medium | deep | dark

COLOR HUE:
WHITE: greenish | yellow | straw yellow | gold | amber
RED: purplish | ruby | red | garnet | brick | brown
ROSÉ: pink | salmon | orange | copper

CLARITY:
clear | slight haze | cloudy

AROMA INTENSITY:
low | moderate | aromatic | powerful

DEVELOPMENT:
youthful | some age | aged

AROMAS:

DRY/SWEET:
bone dry | dry | off dry | medium sweet | sweet | very sweet

BODY:
very light | light | medium | medium-full | full-bodied | heavy

ACIDITY:
tart | crisp | fresh | smooth | flabby

TANNINS (IF PRESENT):
LEVEL: low | medium | high   TYPE: soft | round | dry | hard

BALANCE:
good | fair | unbalanced (excess: alcohol - acid - tannin - sugar)

FLAVOR INTENSITY:
low | moderate | flavorful | powerful

FLAVORS:

FINISH:
short (< 3 sec) | medium (4-5) | long (5-7) | v. long (>8 sec)

CONCLUSION:

STYLE:
traditional | in-between | modern

rating: ☆ ☆ ☆ ☆ ☆

FOOD: **FOOD PAIRING:**

MATCH: perfect | good | neutral | bad

tasting date: location:

tasting partner(s):

wine name:

producer:

region/appellation:

grape varieties:

vintage: alcohol: price:

COLOR DEPTH:
watery | pale | medium | deep | dark

COLOR HUE:
WHITE: greenish | yellow | straw yellow | gold | amber
RED: purplish | ruby | red | garnet | brick | brown
ROSÉ: pink | salmon | orange | copper

CLARITY:
clear | slight haze | cloudy

AROMA INTENSITY:
low | moderate | aromatic | powerful

DEVELOPMENT:
youthful | some age | aged

AROMAS:

DRY/SWEET:
bone dry | dry | off dry | medium sweet | sweet | very sweet

BODY:
very light | light | medium | medium-full | full-bodied | heavy

ACIDITY:
tart | crisp | fresh | smooth | flabby

TANNINS (IF PRESENT):
LEVEL: low | medium | high   TYPE: soft | round | dry | hard

BALANCE:
good | fair | unbalanced (excess: alcohol - acid - tannin - sugar)

FLAVOR INTENSITY:
low | moderate | flavorful | powerful

FLAVORS:

FINISH:
short (< 3 sec) | medium (4-5) | long (5-7) | v. long (>8 sec)

CONCLUSION:

STYLE:
traditional | in-between | modern

rating: ☆ ☆ ☆ ☆ ☆

FOOD: **FOOD PAIRING:**
                   MATCH: perfect | good | neutral | bad

tasting date: location:

tasting partner(s):

wine name:

producer:

region/appellation:

grape varieties:

vintage: alcohol: price:

COLOR DEPTH:
watery | pale | medium | deep | dark

COLOR HUE:
WHITE: greenish | yellow | straw yellow | gold | amber
RED: purplish | ruby | red | garnet | brick | brown
ROSÉ: pink | salmon | orange | copper

CLARITY:
clear | slight haze | cloudy

AROMA INTENSITY:
low | moderate | aromatic | powerful

DEVELOPMENT:
youthful | some age | aged

AROMAS:

DRY/SWEET:
bone dry | dry | off dry | medium sweet | sweet | very sweet

BODY:
very light | light | medium | medium-full | full-bodied | heavy

ACIDITY:
tart | crisp | fresh | smooth | flabby

TANNINS (IF PRESENT):
LEVEL: low | medium | high   TYPE: soft | round | dry | hard

BALANCE:
good | fair | unbalanced (excess: alcohol - acid - tannin - sugar)

FLAVOR INTENSITY:
low | moderate | flavorful | powerful

FLAVORS:

FINISH:
short (< 3 sec) | medium (4-5) | long (5-7) | v. long (>8 sec)

CONCLUSION:

STYLE:
traditional | in-between | modern

rating: ☆ ☆ ☆ ☆ ☆

FOOD: ## FOOD PAIRING:
MATCH: perfect | good | neutral | bad

tasting date: location:

tasting partner(s):

wine name:

producer:

region/appellation:

grape varieties:

vintage: alcohol: price:

 COLOR DEPTH:
watery | pale | medium | deep | dark

COLOR HUE:
WHITE: greenish | yellow | straw yellow | gold | amber
RED: purplish | ruby | red | garnet | brick | brown
ROSÉ: pink | salmon | orange | copper

CLARITY:
clear | slight haze | cloudy

 AROMA INTENSITY:
low | moderate | aromatic | powerful

DEVELOPMENT:
youthful | some age | aged

AROMAS:

DRY/SWEET:
bone dry | dry | off dry | medium sweet | sweet | very sweet

BODY:
very light | light | medium | medium-full | full-bodied | heavy

ACIDITY:
tart | crisp | fresh | smooth | flabby

TANNINS (IF PRESENT):
LEVEL: low | medium | high TYPE: soft | round | dry | hard

BALANCE:
good | fair | unbalanced (excess: alcohol - acid - tannin - sugar)

FLAVOR INTENSITY:
low | moderate | flavorful | powerful

FLAVORS:

FINISH:
short (< 3 sec) | medium (4-5) | long (5-7) | v. long (>8 sec)

CONCLUSION:

STYLE:
traditional | in-between | modern

rating: ☆ ☆ ☆ ☆ ☆

FOOD: **FOOD PAIRING:**
MATCH: perfect | good | neutral | bad

tasting date: location:

tasting partner(s):

wine name:

producer:

region/appellation:

grape varieties:

vintage: alcohol: price:

COLOR DEPTH:
watery | pale | medium | deep | dark

COLOR HUE:
WHITE: greenish | yellow | straw yellow | gold | amber
RED: purplish | ruby | red | garnet | brick | brown
ROSÉ: pink | salmon | orange | copper

CLARITY:
clear | slight haze | cloudy

AROMA INTENSITY:
low | moderate | aromatic | powerful

DEVELOPMENT:
youthful | some age | aged

AROMAS:

DRY/SWEET:
bone dry | dry | off dry | medium sweet | sweet | very sweet

BODY:
very light | light | medium | medium-full | full-bodied | heavy

ACIDITY:
tart | crisp | fresh | smooth | flabby

TANNINS (IF PRESENT):
LEVEL: low | medium | high   TYPE: soft | round | dry | hard

BALANCE:
good | fair | unbalanced (excess: alcohol - acid - tannin - sugar)

FLAVOR INTENSITY:
low | moderate | flavorful | powerful

FLAVORS:

FINISH:
short (< 3 sec) | medium (4-5) | long (5-7) | v. long (>8 sec)

CONCLUSION:

STYLE:
traditional | in-between | modern

rating: ☆ ☆ ☆ ☆ ☆

FOOD: **FOOD PAIRING:**

MATCH: perfect | good | neutral | bad

tasting date: location:

tasting partner(s):

wine name:

producer:

region/appellation:

grape varieties:

vintage: alcohol: price:

COLOR DEPTH:
watery | pale | medium | deep | dark

COLOR HUE:
WHITE: greenish | yellow | straw yellow | gold | amber
RED: purplish | ruby | red | garnet | brick | brown
ROSÉ: pink | salmon | orange | copper

CLARITY:
clear | slight haze | cloudy

AROMA INTENSITY:
low | moderate | aromatic | powerful

DEVELOPMENT:
youthful | some age | aged

AROMAS:

DRY/SWEET:
bone dry | dry | off dry | medium sweet | sweet | very sweet

BODY:
very light | light | medium | medium-full | full-bodied | heavy

ACIDITY:
tart | crisp | fresh | smooth | flabby

TANNINS (IF PRESENT):
LEVEL: low | medium | high   TYPE: soft | round | dry | hard

BALANCE:
good | fair | unbalanced (excess: alcohol - acid - tannin - sugar)

FLAVOR INTENSITY:
low | moderate | flavorful | powerful

FLAVORS:

FINISH:
short (< 3 sec) | medium (4-5) | long (5-7) | v. long (>8 sec)

CONCLUSION:

STYLE:
traditional | in-between | modern

rating: ☆ ☆ ☆ ☆ ☆

FOOD: **FOOD PAIRING:**
            MATCH: perfect | good | neutral | bad

tasting date: location:

tasting partner(s):

wine name:

producer:

region/appellation:

grape varieties:

vintage: alcohol: price:

COLOR DEPTH:
watery | pale | medium | deep | dark

COLOR HUE:
WHITE: greenish | yellow | straw yellow | gold | amber
RED: purplish | ruby | red | garnet | brick | brown
ROSÉ: pink | salmon | orange | copper

CLARITY:
clear | slight haze | cloudy

AROMA INTENSITY:
low | moderate | aromatic | powerful

DEVELOPMENT:
youthful | some age | aged

AROMAS:

DRY/SWEET:
bone dry | dry | off dry | medium sweet | sweet | very sweet

BODY:
very light | light | medium | medium-full | full-bodied | heavy

ACIDITY:
tart | crisp | fresh | smooth | flabby

TANNINS (IF PRESENT):
LEVEL: low | medium | high   TYPE: soft | round | dry | hard

BALANCE:
good | fair | unbalanced (excess: alcohol - acid - tannin - sugar)

FLAVOR INTENSITY:
low | moderate | flavorful | powerful

FLAVORS:

FINISH:
short (< 3 sec) | medium (4-5) | long (5-7) | v. long (>8 sec)

CONCLUSION:

STYLE:
traditional | in-between | modern

rating: ☆ ☆ ☆ ☆ ☆

FOOD: **FOOD PAIRING:**

MATCH: perfect | good | neutral | bad

tasting date: location:

tasting partner(s):

wine name:

producer:

region/appellation:

grape varieties:

vintage: alcohol: price:

COLOR DEPTH:
watery | pale | medium | deep | dark

COLOR HUE:
WHITE: greenish | yellow | straw yellow | gold | amber
RED: purplish | ruby | red | garnet | brick | brown
ROSÉ: pink | salmon | orange | copper

CLARITY:
clear | slight haze | cloudy

AROMA INTENSITY:
low | moderate | aromatic | powerful

DEVELOPMENT:
youthful | some age | aged

AROMAS:

DRY/SWEET:
bone dry | dry | off dry | medium sweet | sweet | very sweet

BODY:
very light | light | medium | medium-full | full-bodied | heavy

ACIDITY:
tart | crisp | fresh | smooth | flabby

TANNINS (IF PRESENT):
LEVEL: low | medium | high   TYPE: soft | round | dry | hard

BALANCE:
good | fair | unbalanced (excess: alcohol - acid - tannin - sugar)

FLAVOR INTENSITY:
low | moderate | flavorful | powerful

FLAVORS:

FINISH:
short (< 3 sec) | medium (4-5) | long (5-7) | v. long (>8 sec)

CONCLUSION:

STYLE:
traditional | in-between | modern

rating: ☆ ☆ ☆ ☆ ☆

FOOD: **FOOD PAIRING:**
MATCH: perfect | good | neutral | bad

tasting date: location:

tasting partner(s):

wine name:

producer:

region/appellation:

grape varieties:

vintage: alcohol: price:

COLOR DEPTH:
watery | pale | medium | deep | dark

COLOR HUE:
WHITE: greenish | yellow | straw yellow | gold | amber
RED: purplish | ruby | red | garnet | brick | brown
ROSÉ: pink | salmon | orange | copper

CLARITY:
clear | slight haze | cloudy

AROMA INTENSITY:
low | moderate | aromatic | powerful

DEVELOPMENT:
youthful | some age | aged

AROMAS:

DRY/SWEET:
bone dry | dry | off dry | medium sweet | sweet | very sweet

BODY:
very light | light | medium | medium-full | full-bodied | heavy

ACIDITY:
tart | crisp | fresh | smooth | flabby

TANNINS (IF PRESENT):
LEVEL: low | medium | high   TYPE: soft | round | dry | hard

BALANCE:
good | fair | unbalanced (excess: alcohol - acid - tannin - sugar)

FLAVOR INTENSITY:
low | moderate | flavorful | powerful

FLAVORS:

FINISH:
short (< 3 sec) | medium (4-5) | long (5-7) | v. long (>8 sec)

CONCLUSION:

STYLE:
traditional | in-between | modern

rating: ☆ ☆ ☆ ☆ ☆

FOOD: **FOOD PAIRING:**

           MATCH: perfect | good | neutral | bad

tasting date: location:

tasting partner(s):

wine name:

producer:

region/appellation:

grape varieties:

vintage: alcohol: price:

COLOR DEPTH:
watery | pale | medium | deep | dark
COLOR HUE:
WHITE: greenish | yellow | straw yellow | gold | amber
RED: purplish | ruby | red | garnet | brick | brown
ROSÉ: pink | salmon | orange | copper
CLARITY:
clear | slight haze | cloudy

AROMA INTENSITY:
low | moderate | aromatic | powerful
DEVELOPMENT:
youthful | some age | aged
AROMAS:

DRY/SWEET:
bone dry | dry | off dry | medium sweet | sweet | very sweet
BODY:
very light | light | medium | medium-full | full-bodied | heavy
ACIDITY:
tart | crisp | fresh | smooth | flabby
TANNINS (IF PRESENT):
LEVEL: low | medium | high   TYPE: soft | round | dry | hard
BALANCE:
good | fair | unbalanced (excess: alcohol - acid - tannin - sugar)
FLAVOR INTENSITY:
low | moderate | flavorful | powerful
FLAVORS:

FINISH:
short (< 3 sec) | medium (4-5) | long (5-7) | v. long (>8 sec)
CONCLUSION:

STYLE:
traditional | in-between | modern
rating: ☆ ☆ ☆ ☆ ☆

FOOD: **FOOD PAIRING:**
MATCH: perfect | good | neutral | bad

tasting date: location:

tasting partner(s):

wine name:

producer:

region/appellation:

grape varieties:

vintage: alcohol: price:

 COLOR DEPTH:
watery | pale | medium | deep | dark

COLOR HUE:
WHITE: greenish | yellow | straw yellow | gold | amber
RED: purplish | ruby | red | garnet | brick | brown
ROSÉ: pink | salmon | orange | copper

CLARITY:
clear | slight haze | cloudy

 AROMA INTENSITY:
low | moderate | aromatic | powerful

DEVELOPMENT:
youthful | some age | aged

AROMAS:

 DRY/SWEET:
bone dry | dry | off dry | medium sweet | sweet | very sweet

BODY:
very light | light | medium | medium-full | full-bodied | heavy

ACIDITY:
tart | crisp | fresh | smooth | flabby

TANNINS (IF PRESENT):
LEVEL: low | medium | high   TYPE: soft | round | dry | hard

BALANCE:
good | fair | unbalanced (excess: alcohol - acid - tannin - sugar)

FLAVOR INTENSITY:
low | moderate | flavorful | powerful

FLAVORS:

FINISH:
short (< 3 sec) | medium (4-5) | long (5-7) | v. long (>8 sec)

CONCLUSION:

STYLE:
traditional | in-between | modern

rating: ☆ ☆ ☆ ☆ ☆

FOOD: **FOOD PAIRING:**
                 MATCH: perfect | good | neutral | bad

tasting date: location:

tasting partner(s):

wine name:

producer:

region/appellation:

grape varieties:

vintage: alcohol: price:

COLOR DEPTH:
watery | pale | medium | deep | dark

COLOR HUE:
WHITE: greenish | yellow | straw yellow | gold | amber
RED: purplish | ruby | red | garnet | brick | brown
ROSÉ: pink | salmon | orange | copper

CLARITY:
clear | slight haze | cloudy

AROMA INTENSITY:
low | moderate | aromatic | powerful

DEVELOPMENT:
youthful | some age | aged

AROMAS:

DRY/SWEET:
bone dry | dry | off dry | medium sweet | sweet | very sweet

BODY:
very light | light | medium | medium-full | full-bodied | heavy

ACIDITY:
tart | crisp | fresh | smooth | flabby

TANNINS (IF PRESENT):
LEVEL: low | medium | high   TYPE: soft | round | dry | hard

BALANCE:
good | fair | unbalanced (excess: alcohol - acid - tannin - sugar)

FLAVOR INTENSITY:
low | moderate | flavorful | powerful

FLAVORS:

FINISH:
short (< 3 sec) | medium (4-5) | long (5-7) | v. long (>8 sec)

CONCLUSION:

STYLE:
traditional | in-between | modern

rating: ☆ ☆ ☆ ☆ ☆

FOOD: ### FOOD PAIRING:
MATCH: perfect | good | neutral | bad

tasting date: location:

tasting partner(s):

wine name:

producer:

region/appellation:

grape varieties:

vintage: alcohol: price:

COLOR DEPTH:
watery | pale | medium | deep | dark

COLOR HUE:
WHITE: greenish | yellow | straw yellow | gold | amber
RED: purplish | ruby | red | garnet | brick | brown
ROSÉ: pink | salmon | orange | copper

CLARITY:
clear | slight haze | cloudy

AROMA INTENSITY:
low | moderate | aromatic | powerful

DEVELOPMENT:
youthful | some age | aged

AROMAS:

DRY/SWEET:
bone dry | dry | off dry | medium sweet | sweet | very sweet

BODY:
very light | light | medium | medium-full | full-bodied | heavy

ACIDITY:
tart | crisp | fresh | smooth | flabby

TANNINS (IF PRESENT):
LEVEL: low | medium | high   TYPE: soft | round | dry | hard

BALANCE:
good | fair | unbalanced (excess: alcohol - acid - tannin - sugar)

FLAVOR INTENSITY:
low | moderate | flavorful | powerful

FLAVORS:

FINISH:
short (< 3 sec) | medium (4-5) | long (5-7) | v. long (>8 sec)

CONCLUSION:

STYLE:
traditional | in-between | modern

rating: ☆ ☆ ☆ ☆ ☆

FOOD: **FOOD PAIRING:**
                MATCH: perfect | good | neutral | bad

tasting date: location:

tasting partner(s):

wine name:

producer:

region/appellation:

grape varieties:

vintage: alcohol: price:

COLOR DEPTH:
watery | pale | medium | deep | dark

COLOR HUE:
WHITE: greenish | yellow | straw yellow | gold | amber
RED: purplish | ruby | red | garnet | brick | brown
ROSÉ: pink | salmon | orange | copper

CLARITY:
clear | slight haze | cloudy

AROMA INTENSITY:
low | moderate | aromatic | powerful

DEVELOPMENT:
youthful | some age | aged

AROMAS:

DRY/SWEET:
bone dry | dry | off dry | medium sweet | sweet | very sweet

BODY:
very light | light | medium | medium-full | full-bodied | heavy

ACIDITY:
tart | crisp | fresh | smooth | flabby

TANNINS (IF PRESENT):
LEVEL: low | medium | high   TYPE: soft | round | dry | hard

BALANCE:
good | fair | unbalanced (excess: alcohol - acid - tannin - sugar)

FLAVOR INTENSITY:
low | moderate | flavorful | powerful

FLAVORS:

FINISH:
short (< 3 sec) | medium (4-5) | long (5-7) | v. long (>8 sec)

CONCLUSION:

STYLE:
traditional | in-between | modern

rating: ☆ ☆ ☆ ☆ ☆

FOOD: ### FOOD PAIRING:
MATCH: perfect | good | neutral | bad

tasting date: location:

tasting partner(s):

wine name:

producer:

region/appellation:

grape varieties:

vintage: alcohol: price:

COLOR DEPTH:
watery | pale | medium | deep | dark

COLOR HUE:
WHITE: greenish | yellow | straw yellow | gold | amber
RED: purplish | ruby | red | garnet | brick | brown
ROSÉ: pink | salmon | orange | copper

CLARITY:
clear | slight haze | cloudy

AROMA INTENSITY:
low | moderate | aromatic | powerful

DEVELOPMENT:
youthful | some age | aged

AROMAS:

DRY/SWEET:
bone dry | dry | off dry | medium sweet | sweet | very sweet

BODY:
very light | light | medium | medium-full | full-bodied | heavy

ACIDITY:
tart | crisp | fresh | smooth | flabby

TANNINS (IF PRESENT):
LEVEL: low | medium | high   TYPE: soft | round | dry | hard

BALANCE:
good | fair | unbalanced (excess: alcohol - acid - tannin - sugar)

FLAVOR INTENSITY:
low | moderate | flavorful | powerful

FLAVORS:

FINISH:
short (< 3 sec) | medium (4-5) | long (5-7) | v. long (>8 sec)

CONCLUSION:

STYLE:
traditional | in-between | modern

rating: ☆ ☆ ☆ ☆ ☆

FOOD: **FOOD PAIRING:**

MATCH: perfect | good | neutral | bad

tasting date: location:

tasting partner(s):

wine name:

producer:

region/appellation:

grape varieties:

vintage: alcohol: price:

COLOR DEPTH:
watery | pale | medium | deep | dark

COLOR HUE:
WHITE: greenish | yellow | straw yellow | gold | amber
RED: purplish | ruby | red | garnet | brick | brown
ROSÉ: pink | salmon | orange | copper

CLARITY:
clear | slight haze | cloudy

AROMA INTENSITY:
low | moderate | aromatic | powerful

DEVELOPMENT:
youthful | some age | aged

AROMAS:

DRY/SWEET:
bone dry | dry | off dry | medium sweet | sweet | very sweet

BODY:
very light | light | medium | medium-full | full-bodied | heavy

ACIDITY:
tart | crisp | fresh | smooth | flabby

TANNINS (IF PRESENT):
LEVEL: low | medium | high   TYPE: soft | round | dry | hard

BALANCE:
good | fair | unbalanced (excess: alcohol - acid - tannin - sugar)

FLAVOR INTENSITY:
low | moderate | flavorful | powerful

FLAVORS:

FINISH:
short (< 3 sec) | medium (4-5) | long (5-7) | v. long (>8 sec)

CONCLUSION:

STYLE:
traditional | in-between | modern

rating: ☆ ☆ ☆ ☆ ☆

FOOD: ## FOOD PAIRING:
                  MATCH: perfect | good | neutral | bad

tasting date: location:

tasting partner(s):

wine name:

producer:

region/appellation:

grape varieties:

vintage: alcohol: price:

COLOR DEPTH:
watery | pale | medium | deep | dark

COLOR HUE:
WHITE: greenish | yellow | straw yellow | gold | amber
RED: purplish | ruby | red | garnet | brick | brown
ROSÉ: pink | salmon | orange | copper

CLARITY:
clear | slight haze | cloudy

AROMA INTENSITY:
low | moderate | aromatic | powerful

DEVELOPMENT:
youthful | some age | aged

AROMAS:

DRY/SWEET:
bone dry | dry | off dry | medium sweet | sweet | very sweet

BODY:
very light | light | medium | medium-full | full-bodied | heavy

ACIDITY:
tart | crisp | fresh | smooth | flabby

TANNINS (IF PRESENT):
LEVEL: low | medium | high   TYPE: soft | round | dry | hard

BALANCE:
good | fair | unbalanced (excess: alcohol - acid - tannin - sugar)

FLAVOR INTENSITY:
low | moderate | flavorful | powerful

FLAVORS:

FINISH:
short (< 3 sec) | medium (4-5) | long (5-7) | v. long (>8 sec)

CONCLUSION:

STYLE:
traditional | in-between | modern

rating: ☆ ☆ ☆ ☆ ☆

FOOD: **FOOD PAIRING:**
                MATCH: perfect | good | neutral | bad

tasting date: location:

tasting partner(s):

wine name:

producer:

region/appellation:

grape varieties:

vintage: alcohol: price:

COLOR DEPTH:
watery | pale | medium | deep | dark

COLOR HUE:
WHITE: greenish | yellow | straw yellow | gold | amber
RED: purplish | ruby | red | garnet | brick | brown
ROSÉ: pink | salmon | orange | copper

CLARITY:
clear | slight haze | cloudy

AROMA INTENSITY:
low | moderate | aromatic | powerful

DEVELOPMENT:
youthful | some age | aged

AROMAS:

DRY/SWEET:
bone dry | dry | off dry | medium sweet | sweet | very sweet

BODY:
very light | light | medium | medium-full | full-bodied | heavy

ACIDITY:
tart | crisp | fresh | smooth | flabby

TANNINS (IF PRESENT):
LEVEL: low | medium | high   TYPE: soft | round | dry | hard

BALANCE:
good | fair | unbalanced (excess: alcohol - acid - tannin - sugar)

FLAVOR INTENSITY:
low | moderate | flavorful | powerful

FLAVORS:

FINISH:
short (< 3 sec) | medium (4-5) | long (5-7) | v. long (>8 sec)

CONCLUSION:

STYLE:
traditional | in-between | modern

rating: ☆ ☆ ☆ ☆ ☆

FOOD: **FOOD PAIRING:**
              MATCH: perfect | good | neutral | bad

tasting date: location:

tasting partner(s):

wine name:

producer:

region/appellation:

grape varieties:

vintage: alcohol: price:

 COLOR DEPTH:
watery | pale | medium | deep | dark

COLOR HUE:
WHITE: greenish | yellow | straw yellow | gold | amber
RED: purplish | ruby | red | garnet | brick | brown
ROSÉ: pink | salmon | orange | copper

CLARITY:
clear | slight haze | cloudy

 AROMA INTENSITY:
low | moderate | aromatic | powerful

DEVELOPMENT:
youthful | some age | aged

AROMAS:

 DRY/SWEET:
bone dry | dry | off dry | medium sweet | sweet | very sweet

BODY:
very light | light | medium | medium-full | full-bodied | heavy

ACIDITY:
tart | crisp | fresh | smooth | flabby

TANNINS (IF PRESENT):
LEVEL: low | medium | high   TYPE: soft | round | dry | hard

BALANCE:
good | fair | unbalanced (excess: alcohol - acid - tannin - sugar)

FLAVOR INTENSITY:
low | moderate | flavorful | powerful

FLAVORS:

FINISH:
short (< 3 sec) | medium (4-5) | long (5-7) | v. long (>8 sec)

CONCLUSION:

STYLE:
traditional | in-between | modern

rating: ☆ ☆ ☆ ☆ ☆

FOOD: **FOOD PAIRING:**
MATCH: perfect | good | neutral | bad

tasting date: location:

tasting partner(s):

wine name:

producer:

region/appellation:

grape varieties:

vintage: alcohol: price:

COLOR DEPTH:
watery | pale | medium | deep | dark

COLOR HUE:
WHITE: greenish | yellow | straw yellow | gold | amber
RED: purplish | ruby | red | garnet | brick | brown
ROSÉ: pink | salmon | orange | copper

CLARITY:
clear | slight haze | cloudy

AROMA INTENSITY:
low | moderate | aromatic | powerful

DEVELOPMENT:
youthful | some age | aged

AROMAS:

DRY/SWEET:
bone dry | dry | off dry | medium sweet | sweet | very sweet

BODY:
very light | light | medium | medium-full | full-bodied | heavy

ACIDITY:
tart | crisp | fresh | smooth | flabby

TANNINS (IF PRESENT):
LEVEL: low | medium | high   TYPE: soft | round | dry | hard

BALANCE:
good | fair | unbalanced (excess: alcohol - acid - tannin - sugar)

FLAVOR INTENSITY:
low | moderate | flavorful | powerful

FLAVORS:

FINISH:
short (< 3 sec) | medium (4-5) | long (5-7) | v. long (>8 sec)

CONCLUSION:

STYLE:
traditional | in-between | modern

rating: ☆ ☆ ☆ ☆ ☆

FOOD: ## FOOD PAIRING:
MATCH: perfect | good | neutral | bad

tasting date: location:

tasting partner(s):

wine name:

producer:

region/appellation:

grape varieties:

vintage: alcohol: price:

COLOR DEPTH:
watery | pale | medium | deep | dark

COLOR HUE:
WHITE: greenish | yellow | straw yellow | gold | amber
RED: purplish | ruby | red | garnet | brick | brown
ROSÉ: pink | salmon | orange | copper

CLARITY:
clear | slight haze | cloudy

AROMA INTENSITY:
low | moderate | aromatic | powerful

DEVELOPMENT:
youthful | some age | aged

AROMAS:

DRY/SWEET:
bone dry | dry | off dry | medium sweet | sweet | very sweet

BODY:
very light | light | medium | medium-full | full-bodied | heavy

ACIDITY:
tart | crisp | fresh | smooth | flabby

TANNINS (IF PRESENT):
LEVEL: low | medium | high   TYPE: soft | round | dry | hard

BALANCE:
good | fair | unbalanced (excess: alcohol - acid - tannin - sugar)

FLAVOR INTENSITY:
low | moderate | flavorful | powerful

FLAVORS:

FINISH:
short (< 3 sec) | medium (4-5) | long (5-7) | v. long (>8 sec)

CONCLUSION:

STYLE:
traditional | in-between | modern

rating: ☆ ☆ ☆ ☆ ☆

FOOD: **FOOD PAIRING:**
MATCH: perfect | good | neutral | bad

tasting date: location:

tasting partner(s):

wine name:

producer:

region/appellation:

grape varieties:

vintage: alcohol: price:

COLOR DEPTH:
watery | pale | medium | deep | dark

COLOR HUE:
WHITE: greenish | yellow | straw yellow | gold | amber
RED: purplish | ruby | red | garnet | brick | brown
ROSÉ: pink | salmon | orange | copper

CLARITY:
clear | slight haze | cloudy

AROMA INTENSITY:
low | moderate | aromatic | powerful

DEVELOPMENT:
youthful | some age | aged

AROMAS:

DRY/SWEET:
bone dry | dry | off dry | medium sweet | sweet | very sweet

BODY:
very light | light | medium | medium-full | full-bodied | heavy

ACIDITY:
tart | crisp | fresh | smooth | flabby

TANNINS (IF PRESENT):
LEVEL: low | medium | high   TYPE: soft | round | dry | hard

BALANCE:
good | fair | unbalanced (excess: alcohol - acid - tannin - sugar)

FLAVOR INTENSITY:
low | moderate | flavorful | powerful

FLAVORS:

FINISH:
short (< 3 sec) | medium (4-5) | long (5-7) | v. long (>8 sec)

CONCLUSION:

STYLE:
traditional | in-between | modern

rating: ☆ ☆ ☆ ☆ ☆

FOOD: **FOOD PAIRING:**

MATCH: perfect | good | neutral | bad

tasting date: location:

tasting partner(s):

wine name:

producer:

region/appellation:

grape varieties:

vintage: alcohol: price:

COLOR DEPTH:
watery | pale | medium | deep | dark

COLOR HUE:
WHITE: greenish | yellow | straw yellow | gold | amber
RED: purplish | ruby | red | garnet | brick | brown
ROSÉ: pink | salmon | orange | copper

CLARITY:
clear | slight haze | cloudy

AROMA INTENSITY:
low | moderate | aromatic | powerful

DEVELOPMENT:
youthful | some age | aged

AROMAS:

DRY/SWEET:
bone dry | dry | off dry | medium sweet | sweet | very sweet

BODY:
very light | light | medium | medium-full | full-bodied | heavy

ACIDITY:
tart | crisp | fresh | smooth | flabby

TANNINS (IF PRESENT):
LEVEL: low | medium | high   TYPE: soft | round | dry | hard

BALANCE:
good | fair | unbalanced (excess: alcohol - acid - tannin - sugar)

FLAVOR INTENSITY:
low | moderate | flavorful | powerful

FLAVORS:

FINISH:
short (< 3 sec) | medium (4-5) | long (5-7) | v. long (>8 sec)

CONCLUSION:

STYLE:
traditional | in-between | modern

rating: ☆ ☆ ☆ ☆ ☆

FOOD: ## FOOD PAIRING:
MATCH: perfect | good | neutral | bad

tasting date: location:

tasting partner(s):

wine name:

producer:

region/appellation:

grape varieties:

vintage: alcohol: price:

COLOR DEPTH:
watery | pale | medium | deep | dark

COLOR HUE:
WHITE: greenish | yellow | straw yellow | gold | amber
RED: purplish | ruby | red | garnet | brick | brown
ROSÉ: pink | salmon | orange | copper

CLARITY:
clear | slight haze | cloudy

AROMA INTENSITY:
low | moderate | aromatic | powerful

DEVELOPMENT:
youthful | some age | aged

AROMAS:

DRY/SWEET:
bone dry | dry | off dry | medium sweet | sweet | very sweet

BODY:
very light | light | medium | medium-full | full-bodied | heavy

ACIDITY:
tart | crisp | fresh | smooth | flabby

TANNINS (IF PRESENT):
LEVEL: low | medium | high   TYPE: soft | round | dry | hard

BALANCE:
good | fair | unbalanced (excess: alcohol - acid - tannin - sugar)

FLAVOR INTENSITY:
low | moderate | flavorful | powerful

FLAVORS:

FINISH:
short (< 3 sec) | medium (4-5) | long (5-7) | v. long (>8 sec)

CONCLUSION:

STYLE:
traditional | in-between | modern

rating: ☆ ☆ ☆ ☆ ☆

FOOD: ### FOOD PAIRING:
MATCH: perfect | good | neutral | bad

tasting date: location:

tasting partner(s):

wine name:

producer:

region/appellation:

grape varieties:

vintage: alcohol: price:

COLOR DEPTH:
watery | pale | medium | deep | dark

COLOR HUE:
WHITE: greenish | yellow | straw yellow | gold | amber
RED: purplish | ruby | red | garnet | brick | brown
ROSÉ: pink | salmon | orange | copper

CLARITY:
clear | slight haze | cloudy

AROMA INTENSITY:
low | moderate | aromatic | powerful

DEVELOPMENT:
youthful | some age | aged

AROMAS:

DRY/SWEET:
bone dry | dry | off dry | medium sweet | sweet | very sweet

BODY:
very light | light | medium | medium-full | full-bodied | heavy

ACIDITY:
tart | crisp | fresh | smooth | flabby

TANNINS (IF PRESENT):
LEVEL: low | medium | high   TYPE: soft | round | dry | hard

BALANCE:
good | fair | unbalanced (excess: alcohol - acid - tannin - sugar)

FLAVOR INTENSITY:
low | moderate | flavorful | powerful

FLAVORS:

FINISH:
short (< 3 sec) | medium (4-5) | long (5-7) | v. long (>8 sec)

CONCLUSION:

STYLE:
traditional | in-between | modern

rating: ☆ ☆ ☆ ☆ ☆

FOOD: **FOOD PAIRING:**

MATCH: perfect | good | neutral | bad

tasting date: location:

tasting partner(s):

wine name:

producer:

region/appellation:

grape varieties:

vintage: alcohol: price:

COLOR DEPTH:
watery | pale | medium | deep | dark

COLOR HUE:
WHITE: greenish | yellow | straw yellow | gold | amber
RED: purplish | ruby | red | garnet | brick | brown
ROSÉ: pink | salmon | orange | copper

CLARITY:
clear | slight haze | cloudy

AROMA INTENSITY:
low | moderate | aromatic | powerful

DEVELOPMENT:
youthful | some age | aged

AROMAS:

DRY/SWEET:
bone dry | dry | off dry | medium sweet | sweet | very sweet

BODY:
very light | light | medium | medium-full | full-bodied | heavy

ACIDITY:
tart | crisp | fresh | smooth | flabby

TANNINS (IF PRESENT):
LEVEL: low | medium | high   TYPE: soft | round | dry | hard

BALANCE:
good | fair | unbalanced (excess: alcohol - acid - tannin - sugar)

FLAVOR INTENSITY:
low | moderate | flavorful | powerful

FLAVORS:

FINISH:
short (< 3 sec) | medium (4-5) | long (5-7) | v. long (>8 sec)

CONCLUSION:

STYLE:
traditional | in-between | modern

rating: ☆ ☆ ☆ ☆ ☆

FOOD: **FOOD PAIRING:**
                  MATCH: perfect | good | neutral | bad

tasting date: location:

tasting partner(s):

wine name:

producer:

region/appellation:

grape varieties:

vintage: alcohol: price:

COLOR DEPTH:
watery | pale | medium | deep | dark

COLOR HUE:
WHITE: greenish | yellow | straw yellow | gold | amber
RED: purplish | ruby | red | garnet | brick | brown
ROSÉ: pink | salmon | orange | copper

CLARITY:
clear | slight haze | cloudy

AROMA INTENSITY:
low | moderate | aromatic | powerful

DEVELOPMENT:
youthful | some age | aged

AROMAS:

DRY/SWEET:
bone dry | dry | off dry | medium sweet | sweet | very sweet

BODY:
very light | light | medium | medium-full | full-bodied | heavy

ACIDITY:
tart | crisp | fresh | smooth | flabby

TANNINS (IF PRESENT):
LEVEL: low | medium | high   TYPE: soft | round | dry | hard

BALANCE:
good | fair | unbalanced (excess: alcohol - acid - tannin - sugar)

FLAVOR INTENSITY:
low | moderate | flavorful | powerful

FLAVORS:

FINISH:
short (< 3 sec) | medium (4-5) | long (5-7) | v. long (>8 sec)

CONCLUSION:

STYLE:
traditional | in-between | modern

rating: ☆ ☆ ☆ ☆ ☆

FOOD: ## FOOD PAIRING:
MATCH: perfect | good | neutral | bad

tasting date: location:

tasting partner(s):

wine name:

producer:

region/appellation:

grape varieties:

vintage: alcohol: price:

COLOR DEPTH:
watery | pale | medium | deep | dark

COLOR HUE:
WHITE: greenish | yellow | straw yellow | gold | amber
RED: purplish | ruby | red | garnet | brick | brown
ROSÉ: pink | salmon | orange | copper

CLARITY:
clear | slight haze | cloudy

AROMA INTENSITY:
low | moderate | aromatic | powerful

DEVELOPMENT:
youthful | some age | aged

AROMAS:

DRY/SWEET:
bone dry | dry | off dry | medium sweet | sweet | very sweet

BODY:
very light | light | medium | medium-full | full-bodied | heavy

ACIDITY:
tart | crisp | fresh | smooth | flabby

TANNINS (IF PRESENT):
LEVEL: low | medium | high   TYPE: soft | round | dry | hard

BALANCE:
good | fair | unbalanced (excess: alcohol - acid - tannin - sugar)

FLAVOR INTENSITY:
low | moderate | flavorful | powerful

FLAVORS:

FINISH:
short (< 3 sec) | medium (4-5) | long (5-7) | v. long (>8 sec)

CONCLUSION:

STYLE:
traditional | in-between | modern

rating: ☆ ☆ ☆ ☆ ☆

FOOD: ## FOOD PAIRING:
                   MATCH: perfect | good | neutral | bad

tasting date: location:

tasting partner(s):

wine name:

producer:

region/appellation:

grape varieties:

vintage: alcohol: price:

COLOR DEPTH:
watery | pale | medium | deep | dark
COLOR HUE:
WHITE: greenish | yellow | straw yellow | gold | amber
RED: purplish | ruby | red | garnet | brick | brown
ROSÉ: pink | salmon | orange | copper
CLARITY:
clear | slight haze | cloudy

AROMA INTENSITY:
low | moderate | aromatic | powerful
DEVELOPMENT:
youthful | some age | aged
AROMAS:

DRY/SWEET:
bone dry | dry | off dry | medium sweet | sweet | very sweet
BODY:
very light | light | medium | medium-full | full-bodied | heavy
ACIDITY:
tart | crisp | fresh | smooth | flabby
TANNINS (IF PRESENT):
LEVEL: low | medium | high   TYPE: soft | round | dry | hard
BALANCE:
good | fair | unbalanced (excess: alcohol - acid - tannin - sugar)
FLAVOR INTENSITY:
low | moderate | flavorful | powerful
FLAVORS:

FINISH:
short (< 3 sec) | medium (4-5) | long (5-7) | v. long (>8 sec)
CONCLUSION:

STYLE:
traditional | in-between | modern
rating: ☆ ☆ ☆ ☆ ☆

FOOD: **FOOD PAIRING:**
                    MATCH: perfect | good | neutral | bad

tasting date: location:

tasting partner(s):

wine name:

producer:

region/appellation:

grape varieties:

vintage: alcohol: price:

COLOR DEPTH:
watery | pale | medium | deep | dark

COLOR HUE:
WHITE: greenish | yellow | straw yellow | gold | amber
RED: purplish | ruby | red | garnet | brick | brown
ROSÉ: pink | salmon | orange | copper

CLARITY:
clear | slight haze | cloudy

AROMA INTENSITY:
low | moderate | aromatic | powerful

DEVELOPMENT:
youthful | some age | aged

AROMAS:

DRY/SWEET:
bone dry | dry | off dry | medium sweet | sweet | very sweet

BODY:
very light | light | medium | medium-full | full-bodied | heavy

ACIDITY:
tart | crisp | fresh | smooth | flabby

TANNINS (IF PRESENT):
LEVEL: low | medium | high   TYPE: soft | round | dry | hard

BALANCE:
good | fair | unbalanced (excess: alcohol - acid - tannin - sugar)

FLAVOR INTENSITY:
low | moderate | flavorful | powerful

FLAVORS:

FINISH:
short (< 3 sec) | medium (4-5) | long (5-7) | v. long (>8 sec)

CONCLUSION:

STYLE:
traditional | in-between | modern

rating: ☆ ☆ ☆ ☆ ☆

FOOD: **FOOD PAIRING:**
                 MATCH: perfect | good | neutral | bad

tasting date: location:

tasting partner(s):

wine name:

producer:

region/appellation:

grape varieties:

vintage: alcohol: price:

COLOR DEPTH:
watery | pale | medium | deep | dark

COLOR HUE:
WHITE: greenish | yellow | straw yellow | gold | amber
RED: purplish | ruby | red | garnet | brick | brown
ROSÉ: pink | salmon | orange | copper

CLARITY:
clear | slight haze | cloudy

AROMA INTENSITY:
low | moderate | aromatic | powerful

DEVELOPMENT:
youthful | some age | aged

AROMAS:

DRY/SWEET:
bone dry | dry | off dry | medium sweet | sweet | very sweet

BODY:
very light | light | medium | medium-full | full-bodied | heavy

ACIDITY:
tart | crisp | fresh | smooth | flabby

TANNINS (IF PRESENT):
LEVEL: low | medium | high   TYPE: soft | round | dry | hard

BALANCE:
good | fair | unbalanced (excess: alcohol - acid - tannin - sugar)

FLAVOR INTENSITY:
low | moderate | flavorful | powerful

FLAVORS:

FINISH:
short (< 3 sec) | medium (4-5) | long (5-7) | v. long (>8 sec)

CONCLUSION:

STYLE:
traditional | in-between | modern

rating: ☆ ☆ ☆ ☆ ☆

FOOD: **FOOD PAIRING:**
                    MATCH: perfect | good | neutral | bad

tasting date: location:

tasting partner(s):

wine name:

producer:

region/appellation:

grape varieties:

vintage: alcohol: price:

COLOR DEPTH:
watery | pale | medium | deep | dark

COLOR HUE:
WHITE: greenish | yellow | straw yellow | gold | amber
RED: purplish | ruby | red | garnet | brick | brown
ROSÉ: pink | salmon | orange | copper

CLARITY:
clear | slight haze | cloudy

AROMA INTENSITY:
low | moderate | aromatic | powerful

DEVELOPMENT:
youthful | some age | aged

AROMAS:

DRY/SWEET:
bone dry | dry | off dry | medium sweet | sweet | very sweet

BODY:
very light | light | medium | medium-full | full-bodied | heavy

ACIDITY:
tart | crisp | fresh | smooth | flabby

TANNINS (IF PRESENT):
LEVEL: low | medium | high   TYPE: soft | round | dry | hard

BALANCE:
good | fair | unbalanced (excess: alcohol - acid - tannin - sugar)

FLAVOR INTENSITY:
low | moderate | flavorful | powerful

FLAVORS:

FINISH:
short (< 3 sec) | medium (4-5) | long (5-7) | v. long (>8 sec)

CONCLUSION:

STYLE:
traditional | in-between | modern

rating: ☆ ☆ ☆ ☆ ☆

FOOD: **FOOD PAIRING:**
MATCH: perfect | good | neutral | bad

tasting date: location:

tasting partner(s):

wine name:

producer:

region/appellation:

grape varieties:

vintage: alcohol: price:

COLOR DEPTH:
watery | pale | medium | deep | dark

COLOR HUE:
WHITE: greenish | yellow | straw yellow | gold | amber
RED: purplish | ruby | red | garnet | brick | brown
ROSÉ: pink | salmon | orange | copper

CLARITY:
clear | slight haze | cloudy

AROMA INTENSITY:
low | moderate | aromatic | powerful

DEVELOPMENT:
youthful | some age | aged

AROMAS:

DRY/SWEET:
bone dry | dry | off dry | medium sweet | sweet | very sweet

BODY:
very light | light | medium | medium-full | full-bodied | heavy

ACIDITY:
tart | crisp | fresh | smooth | flabby

TANNINS (IF PRESENT):
LEVEL: low | medium | high   TYPE: soft | round | dry | hard

BALANCE:
good | fair | unbalanced (excess: alcohol - acid - tannin - sugar)

FLAVOR INTENSITY:
low | moderate | flavorful | powerful

FLAVORS:

FINISH:
short (< 3 sec) | medium (4-5) | long (5-7) | v. long (>8 sec)

CONCLUSION:

STYLE:
traditional | in-between | modern

rating: ☆ ☆ ☆ ☆ ☆

FOOD: **FOOD PAIRING:**

MATCH: perfect | good | neutral | bad

tasting date: location:

tasting partner(s):

wine name:

producer:

region/appellation:

grape varieties:

vintage: alcohol: price:

COLOR DEPTH:
watery | pale | medium | deep | dark

COLOR HUE:
WHITE: greenish | yellow | straw yellow | gold | amber
RED: purplish | ruby | red | garnet | brick | brown
ROSÉ: pink | salmon | orange | copper

CLARITY:
clear | slight haze | cloudy

AROMA INTENSITY:
low | moderate | aromatic | powerful

DEVELOPMENT:
youthful | some age | aged

AROMAS:

DRY/SWEET:
bone dry | dry | off dry | medium sweet | sweet | very sweet

BODY:
very light | light | medium | medium-full | full-bodied | heavy

ACIDITY:
tart | crisp | fresh | smooth | flabby

TANNINS (IF PRESENT):
LEVEL: low | medium | high   TYPE: soft | round | dry | hard

BALANCE:
good | fair | unbalanced (excess: alcohol - acid - tannin - sugar)

FLAVOR INTENSITY:
low | moderate | flavorful | powerful

FLAVORS:

FINISH:
short (< 3 sec) | medium (4-5) | long (5-7) | v. long (>8 sec)

CONCLUSION:

STYLE:
traditional | in-between | modern

rating: ☆ ☆ ☆ ☆ ☆

FOOD: ## FOOD PAIRING:
MATCH: perfect | good | neutral | bad

tasting date: location:

tasting partner(s):

wine name:

producer:

region/appellation:

grape varieties:

vintage: alcohol: price:

 COLOR DEPTH:
watery | pale | medium | deep | dark

COLOR HUE:
WHITE: greenish | yellow | straw yellow | gold | amber
RED: purplish | ruby | red | garnet | brick | brown
ROSÉ: pink | salmon | orange | copper

CLARITY:
clear | slight haze | cloudy

 AROMA INTENSITY:
low | moderate | aromatic | powerful

DEVELOPMENT:
youthful | some age | aged

AROMAS:

 DRY/SWEET:
bone dry | dry | off dry | medium sweet | sweet | very sweet

BODY:
very light | light | medium | medium-full | full-bodied | heavy

ACIDITY:
tart | crisp | fresh | smooth | flabby

TANNINS (IF PRESENT):
LEVEL: low | medium | high   TYPE: soft | round | dry | hard

BALANCE:
good | fair | unbalanced (excess: alcohol - acid - tannin - sugar)

FLAVOR INTENSITY:
low | moderate | flavorful | powerful

FLAVORS:

FINISH:
short (< 3 sec) | medium (4-5) | long (5-7) | v. long (>8 sec)

CONCLUSION:

STYLE:
traditional | in-between | modern

rating: ☆ ☆ ☆ ☆ ☆

FOOD: **FOOD PAIRING:**
                  MATCH: perfect | good | neutral | bad

tasting date: location:

tasting partner(s):

wine name:

producer:

region/appellation:

grape varieties:

vintage: alcohol: price:

COLOR DEPTH:
watery | pale | medium | deep | dark

COLOR HUE:
WHITE: greenish | yellow | straw yellow | gold | amber
RED: purplish | ruby | red | garnet | brick | brown
ROSÉ: pink | salmon | orange | copper

CLARITY:
clear | slight haze | cloudy

AROMA INTENSITY:
low | moderate | aromatic | powerful

DEVELOPMENT:
youthful | some age | aged

AROMAS:

DRY/SWEET:
bone dry | dry | off dry | medium sweet | sweet | very sweet

BODY:
very light | light | medium | medium-full | full-bodied | heavy

ACIDITY:
tart | crisp | fresh | smooth | flabby

TANNINS (IF PRESENT):
LEVEL: low | medium | high   TYPE: soft | round | dry | hard

BALANCE:
good | fair | unbalanced (excess: alcohol - acid - tannin - sugar)

FLAVOR INTENSITY:
low | moderate | flavorful | powerful

FLAVORS:

FINISH:
short (< 3 sec) | medium (4-5) | long (5-7) | v. long (>8 sec)

CONCLUSION:

STYLE:
traditional | in-between | modern

rating: ☆ ☆ ☆ ☆ ☆

FOOD: ## FOOD PAIRING:
MATCH: perfect | good | neutral | bad

tasting date: location:

tasting partner(s):

wine name:

producer:

region/appellation:

grape varieties:

vintage: alcohol: price:

COLOR DEPTH:
watery | pale | medium | deep | dark

COLOR HUE:
WHITE: greenish | yellow | straw yellow | gold | amber
RED: purplish | ruby | red | garnet | brick | brown
ROSÉ: pink | salmon | orange | copper

CLARITY:
clear | slight haze | cloudy

AROMA INTENSITY:
low | moderate | aromatic | powerful

DEVELOPMENT:
youthful | some age | aged

AROMAS:

DRY/SWEET:
bone dry | dry | off dry | medium sweet | sweet | very sweet

BODY:
very light | light | medium | medium-full | full-bodied | heavy

ACIDITY:
tart | crisp | fresh | smooth | flabby

TANNINS (IF PRESENT):
LEVEL: low | medium | high   TYPE: soft | round | dry | hard

BALANCE:
good | fair | unbalanced (excess: alcohol - acid - tannin - sugar)

FLAVOR INTENSITY:
low | moderate | flavorful | powerful

FLAVORS:

FINISH:
short (< 3 sec) | medium (4-5) | long (5-7) | v. long (>8 sec)

CONCLUSION:

STYLE:
traditional | in-between | modern

rating: ☆ ☆ ☆ ☆ ☆

FOOD: **FOOD PAIRING:**

MATCH: perfect | good | neutral | bad

tasting date: location:

tasting partner(s):

wine name:

producer:

region/appellation:

grape varieties:

vintage: alcohol: price:

COLOR DEPTH:
watery | pale | medium | deep | dark

COLOR HUE:
WHITE: greenish | yellow | straw yellow | gold | amber
RED: purplish | ruby | red | garnet | brick | brown
ROSÉ: pink | salmon | orange | copper

CLARITY:
clear | slight haze | cloudy

AROMA INTENSITY:
low | moderate | aromatic | powerful

DEVELOPMENT:
youthful | some age | aged

AROMAS:

DRY/SWEET:
bone dry | dry | off dry | medium sweet | sweet | very sweet

BODY:
very light | light | medium | medium-full | full-bodied | heavy

ACIDITY:
tart | crisp | fresh | smooth | flabby

TANNINS (IF PRESENT):
LEVEL: low | medium | high   TYPE: soft | round | dry | hard

BALANCE:
good | fair | unbalanced (excess: alcohol - acid - tannin - sugar)

FLAVOR INTENSITY:
low | moderate | flavorful | powerful

FLAVORS:

FINISH:
short (< 3 sec) | medium (4-5) | long (5-7) | v. long (>8 sec)

CONCLUSION:

STYLE:
traditional | in-between | modern

rating: ☆ ☆ ☆ ☆ ☆

FOOD: **FOOD PAIRING:**

MATCH: perfect | good | neutral | bad